A Key to
Freshwater Fishes
of the British Isles

WITH NOTES ON THEIR
DISTRIBUTION AND ECOLOGY

by

PETER S. MAITLAND, B.Sc., Ph.D.

The Nature Conservancy, Edinburgh

FRESHWATER BIOLOGICAL ASSOCIATION
SCIENTIFIC PUBLICATION No. 27
1972

FOREWORD

It is perhaps surprising that in a series which is mainly taxonomic in character it should be only the third on the subject of fish that deals with their taxonomy. This probably reflects the difficulty not so much of the subject as of finding an author with the knowledge and enthusiasm to undertake the task. We are therefore specially grateful to Dr Maitland for not only working out this key but also allowing us the use of the data he was in the process of collecting on the distribution of the various species in the waters of the British Isles. Thanks are also due to Dr F. H. Perring and his staff in the Biological Records Centre of the Nature Conservancy for processing these data and producing the maps.

Several, but not all, of the previous publications of this series have, like this one, included Ireland as well as Great Britain in their scope. In these, therefore, the use of the word "British" in titles and elsewhere is according to the dictionaries incorrect. But since there is no single adjective meaning "of the British Isles", we continue in this publication to use the word in that sense.

THE FERRY HOUSE,

February 1972.

H. C. GILSON,

Director.

SBN 900386 18 5

CONTENTS

INTRODUCTION

The large literature on various aspects of the biology of British freshwater fish will not be reviewed here, but many of the more important publications, some of which contain useful bibliographies, are included in the list of references on p. 135. Many of the fish found in this country can often be identified from the illustrations in certain of these publications, but this is a slow and not always accurate method. Moreover most of the older works do not include recently introduced species, such as the largemouth bass. This key is aimed at providing a simple means of identifying accurately any fish found regularly in fresh or brackish water in the British Isles.

Although, having no proper jaws, they are not true fish, the Cyclostomes (Agnatha) are for convenience included in the key together with those fish which, while basically marine, are also found regularly in brackish and fresh waters. Marine species rarely found in brackish water have been excluded, although a few, that might be confused with true brackish-water forms, are mentioned. Most of our freshwater fish are native to these islands, but several introduced species, which have bred and established populations, in some cases over wide areas, have been included. Others, whose status is doubtful, have not, among them various tropical species associated with heated effluents (Meadows, 1968) and temperate species for which there are odd records, but no evidence of the existence of a persistent population.

STRUCTURE

In fish, most of the obvious external sense organs are located on the head: a pair of eyes, the nostrils (normally paired) and often barbels which may vary in number, size and position according to the species (e.g. as in fig. 45). That part of the head anterior to the mouth is normally termed the snout. The position of the mouth itself may be terminal, superior or inferior; in a few species of fish it is modified to form a sucker. Associated with the mouth are several bones of taxonomic importance (*maxillary, premaxillary, vomer* (fig. 10), *hyoid, palatine,* etc.); several of these sometimes carry

4

teeth which may be long or short, permanent or deciduous. In adult lampreys *oral discs* are present which have supra-oral and infra-oral areas bearing teeth (fig. 4). The mouth opens into the pharynx, at the back of which there are, in some fish, bones specialised for chewing and crushing, known as *pharyngeal* bones; the structure of these is important in the identification of the Cyprinidae (fig. 28).

The pharynx leads into the oesophagus which opens, in turn, into the stomach. Food is held for some time in the stomach before being passed into the intestine where it is digested; undigested materials continue into the rectum, from which they pass out through the anus as faeces. Most fish are able to control their buoyancy in the water by means of a swim-bladder which is situated above the gut and in some groups is connected to the oesophagus by a pneumatic duct.

At the sides of the pharynx are cavities leading past the main respiratory organs, the *gills*; together these form the *branchial region* (fig. 24). Each gill consists essentially of a strong supporting arch, on one side of which is a set of comb-like *rakers* whose function is to prevent material passing from the mouth into the delicate blood-filled respiratory *lamellae,* which are aligned on the other side of the gill arch. There are normally four gills on either side, the passages between them leading to the outside of the body through the gill openings; in most species these are protected by a single bony gill cover on either side, known as the *operculum*.

The whole body is covered by skin; in most fish small bony plates known as *scales* lie within this, forming a protective but flexible covering over most areas except the head, which is protected by the head bones themselves. The number and structure of the scales varies from species to species and they are often useful for identification purposes (fig. 64). Some species have no scales; in others they are replaced by isolated bony scutes which project trom the skin. Within the skin too, are pigment cells of various kinds responsible for much of the coloration of the fish. Though colour patterning is useful for distinguishing various species of fish, it should be regarded with caution, for even within a single species the colour can vary greatly with age, sex, season, time of day, or emotional state.

Running along either side of the body in most fish is a *lateral line*; this is a long sensory canal just under the skin but connected to the exterior by a series of pores. These often run through individual scales. The main function of the lateral line is sensory — the fine detection of various kinds of vibration passing through the water.

Branches of the same system run on to the head region.

The typical arrangement of fins on a fish is shown in fig. 1.   There are two sets of paired fins, both situated ventrally, the *pectoral* fins and the *pelvic* fins.   These are equivalent to the fore and hind legs respectively of terrestrial vertebrates.   On the back is a *dorsal* fin; this may occasionally consist of two distinct parts, or be divided into two separate fins, or have the anterior of these represented by several

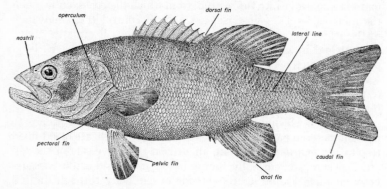

Fig. 1.   General external features of a bony fish.

isolated spines.   Behind the dorsal fin, in the Salmonidae and related families, is a small fleshy fin with no rays, the *adipose* fin. The portion of the body posterior to the anus is known as the *caudal region*.   Ventrally, just behind the anus this bears the *anal* fin, while posteriorly, behind where the body narrows to form the caudal peduncle, is the *caudal fin*.   The supporting structures of fins are known as *rays*; these may be branched or unbranched (when they are usually referred to as spiny or bony) and are often useful taxonomic characters.

COLLECTION AND PRESERVATION

Fish may be caught by a wide variety of methods depending on the species concerned, its size, its habitat, etc.   In the British Isles, among the commonest methods of capture are angling for larger fish and the use of a hand net for smaller fish. There are many other methods of capture (some of them much more efficient, but illegal in most situations) which can be used: e.g. electro-fishing, gill nets, seine nets, trawl nets, traps, etc. These are described in detail elsewhere (Davis, 1936; Rounsefell & Everhardt, 1953; Graham, 1956) and will not be discussed here. Most methods of fishing are highly selective and may often capture only one size-group of one species, and sometimes even only one sex. In carrying out any detailed study of a mixed fish population in a habitat it is normally advisable to use several different methods of capture.

As noted elsewhere, the present major key will not serve to identify the very small specimens (*fry*) of most species. For a short time after hatching the young of most fish change rapidly in form, and features characteristic of the species often do not appear for some time. Unlike many invertebrates, adult fish, because of their large size, can in most cases be identified in the field and there is no need to take them to the laboratory for this purpose. Thus, in very many instances, it is possible to identify specimens correctly immediately after capture and then return them alive to the water. There is little point in killing such fish unless they are required for food, research or some other purpose. In the case of species which are difficult to identify accurately in the field it may be necessary to take them away for detailed examination. It is preferable that they be kept alive for this purpose, but this is often not possible, especially with large or delicate specimens, and most of these fish have to be killed by some means or other. Clearly all specimens must be killed where dissection is essential for their accurate identification.

Apart from asphyxiation, one of the best methods of killing fish without damaging them is to use a liquid anaesthetic, a suitable one being the chemical known as MS222. Specimens dropped into a 0·1% solution of this are narcotised very quickly and can then either be frozen or transferred to a suitable fixative. Fish should be examined as fresh as possible, ideally within 48 hours, or sooner in warm weather. If they cannot be examined within this time they should be either frozen or fixed in some way.

Frozen fish keep their true colours better than fixed ones; the best procedure is to place each specimen in a polythene bag with a little water and a suitable label and freeze the whole as quickly as possible. The fish should be kept straight during this process and care must be taken not to damage its fins.

Even frozen fish will not keep indefinitely, however, if they have to be subjected to periodic thawing for examination purposes, and normally specimens to be stored must be fixed in some way. The most useful fixative is 4% formaldehyde. Each fish should be preserved by placing it flat on its side in a shallow dish with its fins spread as much as possible, and then pouring enough of this solution over it to cover it completely. Specimens should be left for several days to ensure complete fixation. With large fish (more than 30 cm long) it is advisable to make a small slit in the ventral body wall, or to inject the body cavity with a small amount of 40% formaldehyde to ensure complete fixation internally. The fish can then be stored temporarily in polythene bags or permanently in suitable jars, either in 4% formaldehyde or in more pleasant preservatives such as 70% alcohol or 1% propylene phenoxetol (Owen, 1955). Each jar should have inside it a label, written in pencil or indelible ink, with a note of the species concerned, the water where it was collected, the date and the name of the collector.

In situations where the suggested preservatives are not available, quite good results can be got with more easily obtained materials such as: (1) Methylated spirits, diluted 7 parts of spirits to 3 parts of water, (2) salt, 1 part of salt to 2 parts of water, (3) vinegar (acetic acid), as used as a condiment. Preservation can be carried out satisfactorily in polythene bags, keeping the fish as straight as possible.

Eggs or larvae can be preserved and stored in small tubes containing either 4% formaldehyde or 70% alcohol. Labels with relevant data (species, locality, date, colour of eggs when fresh, exact habitat, name of collector, etc.) should be placed inside each tube. In the case of eggs, a reasonable number should be taken where possible, especially if the eggs are adhering to each other, for the form of attachment may be important in identification. This type of material is exceedingly scarce in this country, especially for some species, and the author would be very glad to receive samples of the eggs or larvae of any of the species included in this publication.

Some species of fish can be identified from their scales alone, and in addition it is often possible with several good scales taken from the side of the body (see fig. 1) to establish the specimen's age and certain features of its past history. When scales are available from specimens, they should be placed inside a small envelope which is flattened and then allowed to dry; they will keep indefinitely in this way. The envelope should bear on the outside the following data: species, locality, date, name of collector, and length, weight and sex of the specimen concerned. The length of a fish can be read in a number of different ways; the most useful method is to record the exact distance between the tip of the snout and tip of the middle ray of the tail fin. For identification, the scales should be cleaned and mounted on glass slides, either dry or in glycerine jelly.

As with other vertebrates, bones are often very useful in the identification of fish, and in some cases (e.g. the pharyngeal bones of Cyprinidae and the vomer bones of Salmonidae) they may be essential for accurate identification. Certain bones are also of major importance in providing information on the age and growth of some species (e.g. the opercular bones of Percidae and Esocidae). Preparation of all such bones for examination and subsequent preservation is a relatively simple task; fresh or frozen material should be used, not material which has previously been fixed. The relevant bones should be dissected out from the fish concerned along with their attached tissues. Each bone should be dropped into very hot water for a few minutes and then scrubbed gently with a small stiff brush to clean away soft tissue. The process should be repeated until the bone is completely clean; it can then be placed on clean paper and allowed to dry out slowly in a warm (but not hot) atmosphere. Details concerning the fish from which the bone was removed (species, locality, date, name of collector, length, weight, and sex) should be written either on a small stiff label attached to the bone by strong thread or on the outside of an envelope or small box in which the bone is kept. Bones cleaned and dried in this manner will keep more or less indefinitely.

A great many of the species of freshwater fish which occur in the British Isles can be kept quite successfully in captivity, either indoors in aquaria or outdoors in ponds. The provision of adequate living conditions for such species is a relatively simple matter, the main requirements being reasonable space (with as large a surface area as possible), cool clean water, sufficient cover (in the form of aquatic plants or stones) and appropriate food for the species concerned. The details are not gone into here, for there are several admirable books dealing specifically with the subject of fish-keeping (e.g. Evans, 1952).

NOTES ON THE USE OF THE KEY

Although it is possible with the aid of this key to name to species all fish known to occur in fresh water in the British Isles, a few species are rather difficult to identify accurately without experience, and there is also the possibility of the occurrence of a hybrid (see below) or of a species new to the country. In cases of doubt one or more specimens of the species concerned should be killed and preserved as described above, and then sent together with relevant details to a competent ichthyologist for examination. It is not normally advisable to send fresh fish by post, as they deteriorate too rapidly. When sending preserved fish, they should be drained of preservative, wrapped in damp muslin and then sealed inside a polythene bag. If this is finally placed in a box with packing and parcelled, the fish will travel for several days in perfect condition. The author would be extremely interested to receive any such difficult specimens for examination and verification.

The present key is intended to be as useful as possible in the field so that it may be feasible to return fish to the water alive after capture, examination and identification. During this process specimens should always be kept as cool and as damp as possible. The features used to differentiate families and species are mainly external ones; characters which are as objective and absolute as possible have been selected where feasible. Nevertheless, as noted above, it has been necessary in some instances to resort to characters which involve killing and dissecting the fish; the characters concerned here are mainly found in the region of the head — pharyngeal bones (Cyprinidae), vomer bones (Salmonidae), gills (Clupeidae), etc.

The key follows the dichotomous pattern common to many field keys. Where possible, several distinguishing characters have been used at each point in the key and these should always be considered in combination with each other. Every species is figured and after identification using the text, the relevant figure should be consulted. Due consideration must always be given to the possibility of any specimen being very young, malformed, or a hybrid.

The most common numerical features used in the key are counts of fin rays and of scales. In all the fin ray counts mentioned, the number for each fin is obtained by counting the rays close to the body, before branching occurs. Unbranched rays (spines) are included in these counts. The main scale counts are taken along the lateral line, starting at the first scale behind the operculum and ending at the last scale before the caudal fin. Some diagonal scale counts are also used (fig. 1). These are normally counted from the lateral line up to the adipose fin (where present) and from the lateral line down to the anal fin. Occasionally counts are made from the lateral line up to the dorsal fin and down to the pelvic fin.

Where colours are used in the key they refer to the condition in the fresh fish and should be true irrespective of size (above the larval and fry stages), sex and condition, unless otherwise stated. With many species it is possible to determine the sex accurately only by dissection of the genitalia, especially outwith the breeding season; with others there are constant external sexual differences. These have not been included in the key.

Various species of fish in the British Isles hybridise quite frequently in the wild. Such hybrids are difficult to identify with a key such as this one, as their characters are normally intermediate between those of the two parent species. Unfortunately, owing to the very nature of speciation it is often those species of fish which are most alike (and thus difficult to identify) which are most likely to hybridise. A very wide variety of hybrids has been recorded from Central Europe, but relatively few, mainly Cyprinidae, from the British Isles so far. The list of natural hybrids recorded from Britain follows:

NATURAL HYBRIDS

Salmo trutta	×	*Salvelinus fontinalis*
Cyprinus carpio	×	*Carassius carassius*
Abramis brama	×	*Leuciscus idus*
Abramis brama	×	*Scardinius erythrophthalmus*
Rutilus rutilus	×	*Scardinius erythrophthalmus*
Rutilus rutilus	×	*Abramis brama*
Rutilus rutilus	×	*Alburnus alburnus*
Leuciscus cephalus	×	*Alburnus alburnus*
Leuciscus leuciscus	×	*Alburnus alburnus*
Leuciscus leuciscus	×	*Scardinius erythrophthalmus*

CHECK LIST OF BRITISH SPECIES

Class MARSIPOBRANCHII

Order **Petromyzoniformes**

PETROMYZONIDAE

1. *Petromyzon marinus* Linnaeus, 1758	Marine lamprey
2. *Lampetra fluviatilis* (Linnaeus, 1758)	River lamprey
3. *Lampetra planeri* (Bloch, 1784)	Brook lamprey

Class OSTEICHTHYES

Order **Chondrostei**

ACIPENSERIDAE

4. *Acipenser sturio* Linnaeus, 1758	Sturgeon

Order **Isospondyli**

CLUPEIDAE

5. *Alosa alosa* (Linnaeus, 1758)	Allis shad
6. *Alosa fallax* (Lacépède, 1803)	Twaite shad

SALMONIDAE

7. *Salmo salar* Linnaeus, 1758	Salmon
Salmo trutta Linnaeus, 1758	
8. S. *trutta trutta*	Sea trout
9. S. *trutta fario*	Brown trout
10. *Salmo gairdneri* Richardson, 1836	Rainbow trout
11. *Oncorhynchus gorbuscha* (Walbaum, 1792)	Humpback salmon
12. *Salvelinus alpinus* (Linnaeus, 1758)	Charr
13. *Salvelinus fontinalis* (Mitchill, 1815)	American brook trout, speckled charr

COREGONIDAE

14. *Coregonus lavaretus* (Linnaeus, 1758)	Whitefish
15. *Coregonus albula* (Linnaeus, 1758)	Vendace
16. *Coregonus oxyrinchus* (Linnaeus, 1758)	Houting

THYMALLIDAE

17. *Thymallus thymallus* (Linnaeus, 1758)	Grayling

OSMERIDAE
  18. *Osmerus eperlanus* (Linnaeus, 1758)   Smelt

Order **Haplomi**

ESOCIDAE
  19. *Esox lucius* Linnaeus, 1758   Pike

Order **Ostariophysi**

CYPRINIDAE
  20. *Cyprinus carpio* Linnaeus, 1758   Carp
  21. *Carassius carassius* (Linnaeus, 1758)   Crucian carp
  22. *Carassius auratus* (Linnaeus, 1758)   Goldfish
  23. *Barbus barbus* (Linnaeus, 1758)   Barbel
  24. *Gobio gobio* (Linnaeus, 1758)   Gudgeon
  25. *Tinca tinca* (Linnaeus, 1758)   Tench
  26. *Blicca bjoerkna* (Linnaeus, 1758)   Silver bream
  27. *Abramis brama* (Linnaeus, 1758)   Bream
  28. *Alburnus alburnus* (Linnaeus, 1758)   Bleak
  29. *Phoxinus phoxinus* (Linnaeus, 1758)   Minnow
  30. *Rhodeus sericeus* (Bloch, 1782)   Bitterling
  31. *Scardinius erythrophthalmus* (Linnaeus,
        1758)   Rudd
  32. *Rutilus rutilus* (Linnaeus, 1758)   Roach
  33. *Leuciscus cephalus* (Linnaeus, 1758)   Chub
  34. *Leuciscus idus* (Linnaeus, 1758)   Orfe
  35. *Leuciscus leuciscus* (Linnaeus, 1758)   Dace

COBITIDAE
  36. *Cobitis taenia* Linnaeus 1758   Spined loach
  37. *Noemacheilus barbatulus* (Linnaeus,
        1758)   Stone loach

SILURIDAE
  38. *Silurus glanis* Linnaeus, 1758   Wels

Order **Apodes**

ANGUILLIDAE
  39. *Anguilla anguilla* (Linnaeus, 1758)   Eel

Order **Thoracostei**
GASTEROSTEIDAE
40. *Gasterosteus aculeatus* Linnaeus, 1758   Three-spined
         stickleback
41. *Pungitius pungitius* (Linnaeus, 1758)   Ten-spined
         stickleback

Order **Anacanthini**
GADIDAE
42. *Lota lota* (Linnaeus, 1758)   Burbot

Order **Percomorphi**
SERRANIDAE
43. *Dicentrarchus labrax* (Linnaeus, 1758)   Sea bass

CENTRARCHIDAE
44. *Micropterus salmoides* (Lacépède, 1802)   Largemouth bass
45. *Lepomis gibbosus* (Linnaeus, 1758)   Pumpkinseed
46. *Ambloplites rupestris* (Rafinesque-
    Schmaltz, 1817)   Rock bass

PERCIDAE
47. *Perca fluviatilis* Linnaeus, 1758   Perch
48. *Gymnocephalus cernua* (Linnaeus, 1758)   Ruffe
49. *Stizostedion lucioperca* (Linnaeus, 1758)   Pikeperch, Zander

GOBIIDAE
50. *Pomatoschistus microps* (Krøyer, 1840)   Common goby

MUGILIDAE
51. *Crenimugil labrosus* (Risso, 1826)   Thick-lipped
         mullet
52. *Chelon ramada* (Risso, 1826)   Thin-lipped mullet
53. *Chelon auratus* (Risso, 1810)   Golden mullet

Order **Scleroparei**
COTTIDAE
54. *Cottus gobio* Linnaeus, 1758   Bullhead

Order **Heterosomata**
PLEURONECTIDAE
55. *Platichthys flesus* (Linnaeus, 1758)   Flounder

KEY TO FAMILIES

1 No paired fins. Seven pairs of gill openings. No lower jaw; mouth in adults a sucking disc (fig. 2a). A single median nostril between the eyes—   PETROMYZONIDAE, p. 21

— One or two pairs of fins. One pair of gill openings, each protected by an operculum. Lower jaw present; mouth never a sucking disc. Paired nostrils anterior to the eyes—   2

2 Upper lobe of caudal fin much longer than the lower (heterocercal) (fig. 2b). Five longitudinal rows of large bony plates on the body (fig. 8). Snout greatly elongated—   ACIPENSERIDAE, p. 24

— Caudal fin more or less symmetrical (holocercal). No large bony plates on the body. Snout normal—   3

3 One dorsal fin, or if two, then the posterior one small and fleshy, without rays (adipose). Pelvic fins, where present, approximately midway between pectoral fins and anus. Pneumatic duct present between swimbladder and oesophagus—   4

— Two dorsal fins, or if one, then *either* this is divided into two distinct parts, the anterior part being very spiny or replaced by isolated spines, *or* the body is greatly flattened with both eyes on one side of the head. Pelvic fins just below or only slightly posterior to the pectoral fins. Pneumatic duct absent between swimbladder and oesophagus—   13

4 Barbels on the head present, the largest pair longer than the pectoral fins. Dorsal fin with less than 8 rays. Scales absent (fig. 2k)—   SILURIDAE, p. 24

— Barbels on the head absent, or if present, then much shorter than the pectoral fins. Dorsal fin with more than 8 rays. Scales present (though very small in two families)—   5

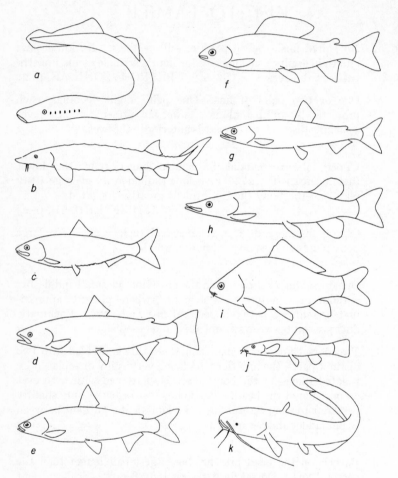

Fig. 2. Outline diagrams of main family types:
a, Petromyzonidae; b, Acipenseridae; c, Clupeidae;
d, Salmonidae; e, Coregonidae; f, Thymallidae; g, Osmeridae;
h, Esocidae; i, Cyprinidae; j, Cobitidae; k, Siluridae;

l, Anguillidae; *m*, Gasterosteidae; *n*, Gadidae; *o*, Serranidae; *p*, Centrarchidae; *q*, Percidae; *r*, Gobiidae; *s*, Mugilidae; *t*, Cottidae; *u*, Pleuronectidae.

5   Two dorsal fins, posterior one fleshy without rays (adipose)—   **6**

—   One dorsal fin—   **9**

6   Scales relatively small, more than 100 along lateral line.   Red pigment often present in the skin (fig. 2*d*)—
                                          SALMONIDAE, p. 25

—   Scales relatively large, less than 100 along lateral line.   Red pigment rarely present in the skin—   **7**

7   Lateral line complete almost to the caudal fin.   Teeth absent or poorly developed.   Pelvic axillary process present (fig. 2*e,f*)—   **8**

—   Lateral line present only for about the first 10 scales.   Teeth well developed.   Pelvic axillary process absent (fig. 2*g*)—
                                          OSMERIDAE, p. 32

8   Dorsal fin large with more than 20 rays, its depressed length much greater than that of the head.   Large black pigment spots normally present in the skin.   Small teeth present (fig. 2*f*)—   THYMALLIDAE, p. 32

—   Dorsal fin normal with less than 20 rays, its depressed length never greater than that of the head.   Large black pigment spots never present in the skin, though small black chromatophores may be common (fig. 2*e*)—   COREGONIDAE, p. 32

9(5)* Dorsal fin distinct from caudal fin.   Pelvic fins present. Body not extremely elongate—   **10**

—   Dorsal fin continuous with caudal and anal fins.   Pelvic fins absent.   Body extremely elongate (fig. 2*l*)—
                                          ANGUILLIDAE, p. 34

10   Scales on the ventral surface keeled.   Lateral line absent. Large elongate scales over the inner part of the caudal fin (fig. 2c)—   CLUPEIDAE, p. 35

---

* Where a couplet is not reached directly from the preceding couplet, the number of the couplet from which the direction came is given thus in parentheses.

— Scales on the ventral surface not keeled.   Lateral line present. No elongate scales over the inner part of the caudal fin—   **11**

11 Head elongate; mouth very large with well-developed teeth. Dorsal fin mostly posterior to the anus (fig. *2h*).   Scales present on head—   ESOCIDAE, p. 36

— Head normal; mouth moderate or small, with teeth absent or poorly developed.   Dorsal fin entirely or mostly anterior to the anus.   Scales absent on head—   **12**

12 Less than five barbels on the head.   Mouth normal.   Scales usually distinct on the body (fig. *2i*)—   CYPRINIDAE, p. 39

— More than five barbels on the head.   Mouth small.   Scales on the body indistinct (fig. *2j*)—   COBITIDAE, p. 52

13(3) Two dorsal fins, *or* if one, then it is divided into two distinct parts, the anterior part being very spiny.   Body never greatly flattened or with isolated spines—   **14**

— One dorsal fin.   Body either greatly flattened or with a row of dorsal spines—   **20**

14 Head with single barbel below the mouth and one small barbel beside each nostril.   Anal fin with more than 60 rays (fig. *2n*)—   GADIDAE, p. 52

— Head without barbels.   Anal fin with less than 60 rays—   **15**

15 Well developed scales over most of the body.   Anterior dorsal fin rays rigid—   **16**

— Scales absent over most of the body (fig. *2t*).   Anterior dorsal fin rays flexible—   COTTIDAE, p. 52

16 Lateral line absent.   Less than five spiny rays in the anterior dorsal fin.   Dorsal fins widely separated, the distance between them always exceeding the length of the longest dorsal ray (fig. *2s*)—   MUGILIDAE, p. 55

— Lateral line present. More than five spiny rays in the anterior dorsal fin. Dorsal fins continuous or close together, the distance between them never exceeding the length of the longest dorsal ray—   **17**

17 Two or fewer anal spines present. Either less than or more than 9 or 10 spiny rays in the first dorsal fin—   **18**

— Three or more anal spines present. 9 or 10 spiny rays in the first dorsal fin—   **19**

18 Two anal spines present. Tail fin forked. More than 10 spiny rays in the first dorsal fin. Pelvic fins not joined medially (fig. 2q)—   PERCIDAE, p. 58

— Anal spines absent. Tail fin rounded. Less than 9 spiny rays in the first dorsal fin. Pelvic fins joined medially (fig. 2r)—
                                                    GOBIIDAE, p. 61

19 (17) Second dorsal fin with one spiny ray anteriorly. Less than 70 scales along the lateral line. Anal fin convex (fig. 2p)—
                                                 CENTRARCHIDAE, p. 61

— Second dorsal fin with three spiny rays anteriorly. More than 70 scales along the lateral line. Anal fin concave (fig. 2o)—
                                                   SERRANIDAE, p. 63

20 (13) Three or more strong spines anterior to the dorsal fin. Body not flattened, eyes on either side of the head. Pelvic fins with less than 3 rays (fig. 2m)—   GASTEROSTEIDAE, p. 64

— No spines anterior to the dorsal fin. Body extremely flattened with both eyes on one side of the head (usually the right). Pelvic fins with more than three rays (fig. 2u)—
                                                PLEURONECTIDAE, p. 65

KEY TO SPECIES

Family PETROMYZONIDAE

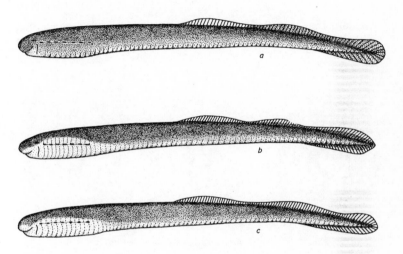

Fig. 3. Ammocoete larvae of Petromyzonidae:
a, *Petromyzon marinus*, Sea lamprey; b, *Lampetra fluviatilis*, River lamprey; c, *Lampetra planeri*, Brook lamprey.

1 Teeth absent, sucker incomplete. Eyes indistinct, covered by skin. Branchial groove present (fig. 3). Skin transparent, dull on the underside—   Ammocoete larvae, 2

— Teeth present, sucker complete. Eyes clearly visible. Branchial groove absent. Skin opaque, silvery-white on underside—
                                      Adults, 4

2   Most of the caudal fin without pigment cells, which occur only
    close to the body (fig. 3c)—   **Lampetra planeri**
                                          Brook lamprey

—   Most of the caudal fin with pigment cells often widely scattered
    in the fin (fig. 3a, b)—   3

3   Less than 60 trunk myomeres.   Branchial region unpigmented
    below the gill slits (fig. 3b)—   **Lampetra fluviatilis**
                                          River lamprey

—   More than 60 trunk myomeres.   Branchial region pigmented
    below the gill slits (fig. 3a)—   **Petromyzon marinus**
                                          Sea lamprey

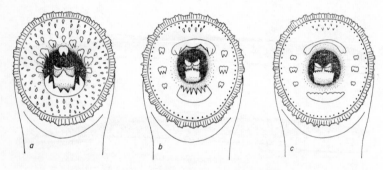

Fig. 4.   Mouth structure of adult Petromyzonidae:
          a, Petromyzon marinus, Sea lamprey;   *b, Lampetra fluviatilis*,
          River lamprey;   *c, Lampetra planeri*, Brook lamprey.

4 (1)* Teeth on the oral disc close together in radiating rows; supra-
       oral dental plate with 2 large teeth (fig. 4a).   Back and sides
       with a marbled pattern.   Length greater than 50 cm—
                                          Petromyzon marinus
                                          Sea lamprey (fig. 5)

* Where a couplet is not reached directly from the preceding couplet, the number
of the couplet from which the direction came is given thus in parentheses.

— Teeth on oral disc widely spaced and not in radiating rows;
supraoral dental plate with, at most, 1 small tooth (fig. 4*b*, *c*).
Back and sides of uniform colour.   Length less than 50 cm—   **5**

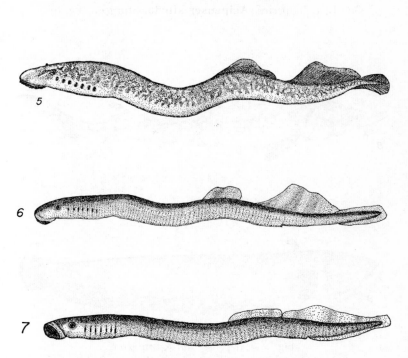

Fig. 5.   *Petromyzon marinus*, Sea lamprey (after Sterba, 1962).
Fig. 6.   *Lampetra fluviatilis*, River lamprey.
Fig. 7.   *Lampetra planeri*, Brook lamprey.

5   Infraoral lamina with 7–10 cusps (fig. 4*b*).   Most teeth strong
and sharp.   Dorsal fins separate—   **Lampetra fluviatilis**
River lamprey (fig. 6)

— Infraoral lamina with 5–9 cusps (fig. 4*c*).   All teeth weak and
blunt.   Dorsal fins connected—   **Lampetra planeri**
Brook lamprey (fig. 7)

Family ACIPENSERIDAE

One British species, **Acipenser sturio,** Sturgeon (fig. 8).

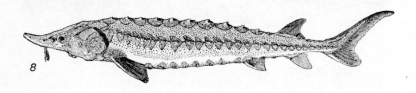

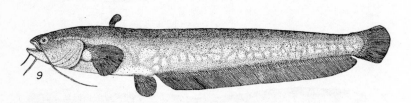

Fig. 8.   *Acipenser sturio,* Sturgeon.
Fig. 9.   *Silurus glanis,* Wels.

Family SILURIDAE

One British species, **Silurus glanis,** Wels (fig. 9).

Family SALMONIDAE

1 More than 12 branched rays in the anal fin, which is longer than high. Vomer long and narrow with weak teeth—
Oncorhynchus gorbuscha
Humpback salmon (fig. 11)

— Less than 12 branched rays in the anal fin, which is higher than long— 2

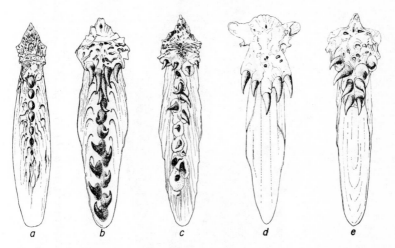

Fig. 10. Vomer bones of Salmonidae:
a, Salmo salar, Salmon; *b, Salmo trutta,* Trout; *c, Salmo gairdneri,* Rainbow trout; *d, Salvelinus alpinus,* Charr; *e, Salvelinus fontinalis,* American brook trout, speckled charr.

2 More than 160 scales along the lateral line. Vomerine teeth confined to the head of the vomer, whose shaft is short and toothless (figs. 10*d, e*)— 3

— Less than 150 scales along the lateral line. Vomerine teeth not confined to the head of the vomer, whose shaft is long with 2 rows of teeth (fig. 10*a, b, c*)— 4

Fig. 11. *Oncorhynchus gorbuscha*, Humpback salmon (female).

3 Hyoid teeth present; premaxillary not toothed on the right side. Back mainly uniformly coloured. Black stripe on the anal fin absent— **Salvelinus alpinus**
Charr (fig. 12)

— Hyoid teeth absent; premaxillary toothed on the right side. Back strongly vermiculated. Black stripe present on the anal fin— **Salvelinus fontinalis**
American brook trout, speckled charr (fig. 13)

Fig. 12. *Salvelinus alpinus,* Charr.
Fig. 13. *Salvelinus fontinalis,* American brook trout, speckled charr.

4 (2) More than 130 scales along the lateral line. No red spots on the body, but a broad pink or red band present along either side. Numerous black spots on the body and fins, especially the adipose and tail fins— **Salmo gairdneri**
Rainbow trout (fig. 14)

— Less than 130 scales along the lateral line. The body may be completely silver, but normally has many black and some red spots present; never a broad red band along either side. Black spots on the adipose and caudal fins ill-defined or absent— **5**

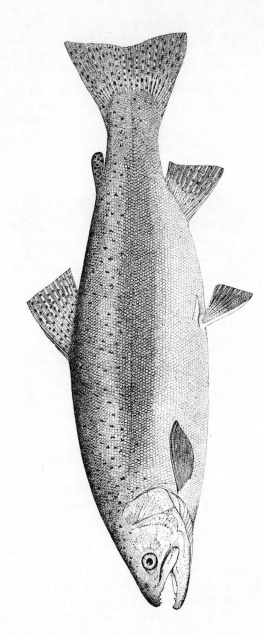

Fig. 14. *Salmo gairdneri*, Rainbow trout.

5 Length usually less than 15 cm. Parr marks (a single line of dark lateral patches) usually present, or body completely silvery (fig. 15). Tail fin distinctly forked—   Juveniles **6**

— Length usually more than 15 cm. Parr marks usually absent (though the body may be well spotted). Tail fin indistinctly or not forked—   Adults **9**

6 Parr marks more or less distinct along the sides; numerous spots present, mostly black but some red—   Fry and parr **7**

— Parr marks indistinct or absent; body almost completely silvery, though a few black spots may be present—   Smolts **8**

7 Parr marks 10–12. A few faint black spots on the dorsal fin which has 10–12 rays. Operculum with less than 3 spots. Adipose fin normally brown. Caudal peduncle thin; tail fin with a deep fork and pointed ends. Pectoral fins large, when stretched back often reaching behind the level of the origin of the dorsal fin. Maxilla reaching to about the middle of the eye—   **Salmo salar**

Salmon (fig. 15*a*)

— Parr marks 9–10.   Many definite black spots on the dorsal fin, which has 8–10 rays.   Operculum with more than 3 black spots.   Adipose fin normally red.   Caudal peduncle thick; tail fin with a shallow fork and rounded ends.   Pectoral fins normal, when stretched back not reaching behind the level of the origin of the dorsal fin.   Maxilla reaching to mid-way between the pupil and rear of the eye—   **Salmo trutta**
Trout (fig. 15*b*)

Fig. 15.   Immature stage (parr) of *Salmo*:
    a, Salmo salar, Salmon;   *b, Salmo trutta,* Trout.

8 (6) Dorsal fin with 10–12 rays.   10–13 scales between the adipose fin and the lateral line.   Operculum with less than 3 spots. Caudal peduncle thin; tail fin with a deep fork.   Pectoral fins large—   **Salmo salar**
Salmon

— Dorsal fin with 8–10 rays. 13–16 scales between the adipose fin and the lateral line. Operculum with more than 3 spots. Caudal peduncle thick; tail fin with a shallow fork. Pectoral fins normal— **Salmo trutta**
Trout

Fig. 16. *Salmo salar*, Salmon (female).
Fig. 17. *Salmo trutta*, Trout.

9 (5) Head of vomer toothless, the shaft poorly toothed with deciduous teeth (fig. 10a). Dorsal fin with 10–12 rays. 10–13 scales between the adipose fin and the lateral line. When laid back, the last ray of the anal fin usually extends about as far posteriorly as the first ray— **Salmo salar**
Salmon (fig. 16)

— Head of vomer toothed, the shaft also well toothed with persistent teeth (fig. 10b). Dorsal fin with 8–10 rays. 13–16 scales between the adipose fin and the lateral line. When laid back, the last ray of the anal fin does not extend as far posteriorly as the first ray— **Salmo trutta**
Trout (fig. 17)

Family OSMERIDAE

One British species, **Osmerus eperlanus,** Smelt (fig. 18).

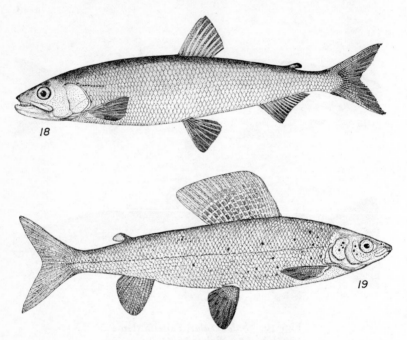

Fig. 18. *Osmerus eperlanus,* Smelt.
Fig. 19. *Thymallus thymallus,* Grayling.

Family THYMALLIDAE

One British species, **Thymallus thymallus,** Grayling (fig. 19).

Family COREGONIDAE

1 Snout conical and produced in front. Distance between the
anterior edge of the eye and the tip of the snout more than twice
the diameter of the eye—   **Coregonus oxyrinchus**
                                   Houting (fig. 20)

— Snout not produced in front. Distance between the anterior edge of the eye and the tip of the snout less than twice the diameter of the eye—   **2**

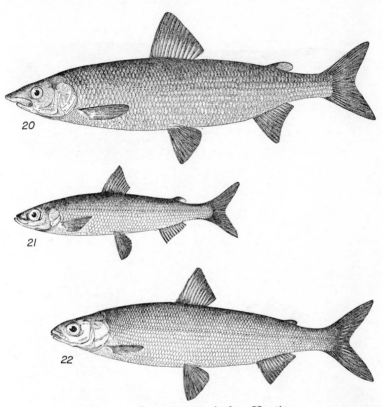

Fig. 20.   *Coregonus oxyrinchus,* Houting.
Fig. 21.   *Coregonus albula,* Vendace, pollan.
Fig. 22.   *Coregonus lavaretus,* Whitefish, schelly, powan, gwyniad.

2   Mouth terminal or superior.   Less than 13 rays in the anal fin—   **Coregonus albula**
Vendace, pollan (fig. 21)

— Mouth inferior.   13 or more rays in the anal fin—
Coregonus lavaretus
Whitefish, schelly, powan, gwyniad (fig. 22)

Family ANGUILLIDAE

One British freshwater species, **Anguilla anguilla,** Eel (fig. 23).

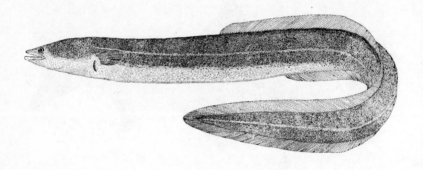

Fig. 23. *Anguilla anguilla,* Eel.

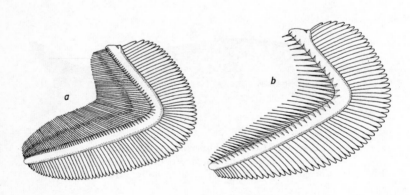

Fig. 24. Gills of Clupeidae:
a, Alosa alosa, Allis shad; *b, Alosa fallax,* Twaite shad.

Family CLUPEIDAE

1 Main longitudinal row of lateral scales numbering less than 70. Less than 60 gill rakers on the first gill arch (fig. 24*b*). A row of dark spots sometimes present along each side—

Alosa fallax
Twaite shad (fig. 25)

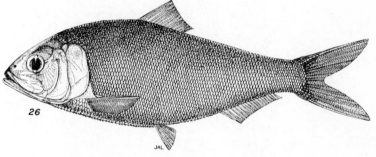

Fig. 25. *Alosa fallax*, Twaite shad.
Fig. 26. *Alosa alosa*, Allis shad.

— Main longitudinal row of lateral scales numbering more than 70. More than 60 gill rakers on the first gill arch (fig. 24*a*). A row of dark spots never present along each side— **Alosa alosa**
Allis shad (fig. 26)

Family ESOCIDAE

One British species, **Esox lucius,** Pike (fig. 27)

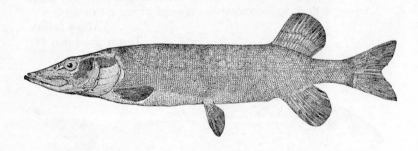

Fig. 27.   *Esox lucius*, Pike.

Fig. 28.   Pharyngeal bones of Cyprinidae:
     a, Cyprinus carpio, Carp;   *b, Carassius carassius,* Crucian carp;   *c, Carassius auratus,* Goldfish;   *d, Barbus barbus,* Barbel;   *e, Gobio gobio,* Gudgeon;   *f, Tinca tinca,* Tench; *g, Blicca bjoerkna,* Silver bream; *h, Abramis brama,* Common bream; *i, Alburnus alburnus,* Bleak;   *j, Phoxinus phoxinus,* Minnow; *k, Rhodeus sericeus,* Bitterling; *l, Scardinius erythrophthalmus,* Rudd;   *m, Rutilus rutilus,* Roach;   *n, Leuciscus cephalus,* Chub; *o, Leuciscus idus,* Orfe; *p, Leuciscus leuciscus,* Dace (after Spillman, 1961).

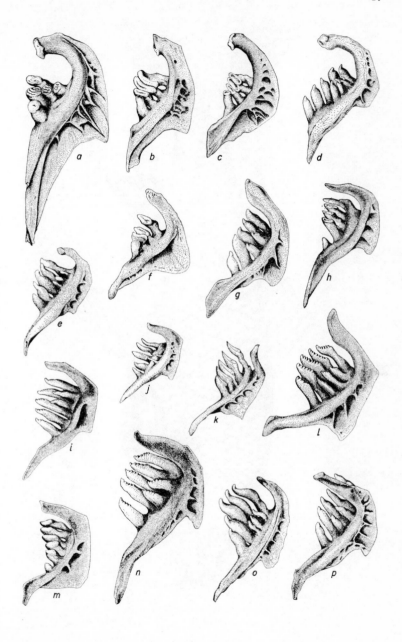

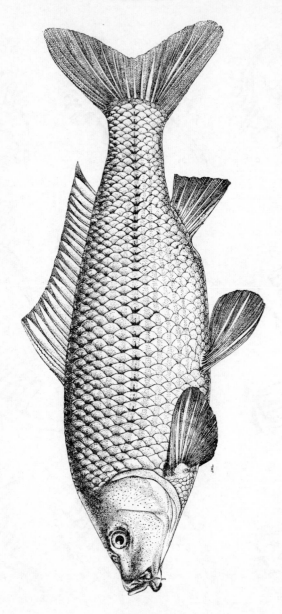

Fig. 29. *Cyprinus carpio*, Carp.

Family CYPRINIDAE

1 Barbels present on the head—   **2**

— Barbels absent on the head—   **5**

2 Dorsal fin with more than 15 rays.   Less than 40 scales along
   the lateral line.   Pharyngeal teeth: 1.1.3:3.1.1 (fig. 28*a*)—
                                                    Cyprinus carpio
                                              Common carp (fig. 29)

— Dorsal fin with less than 15 rays.   More than 40 scales along the
   lateral line.   Pharyngeal teeth not 1.1.3:3.1.1—   **3**

3 Less than 60 scales along the lateral line.   Dorsal fin concave.
   Pharyngeal teeth in two or three rows—   **4**

— More than 90 scales along the lateral line.   Dorsal fin convex.
   Pharyngeal teeth in one row (fig. 28*f*)—   **Tinca tinca**
                                                     Tench (fig. 30)

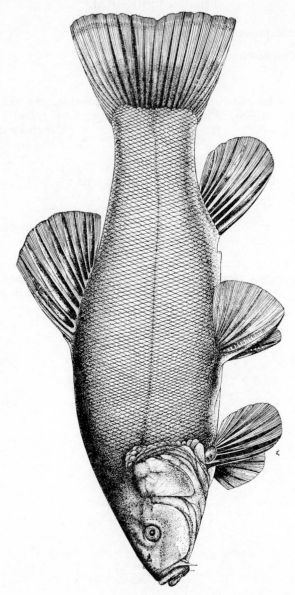

Fig. 30. *Tinca tinca*, Tench.

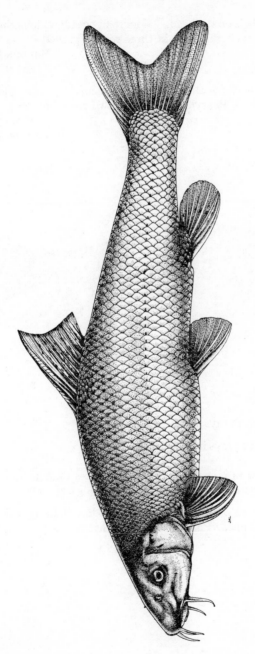

Fig. 31. *Barbus barbus*, Barbel.

4   Four barbels on the head.   More than 50 scales along the lateral
    line.   Pharyngeal teeth in three rows (fig. 28*d*)—

Barbus barbus
Barbel (fig. 31)

—   Two barbels on the head.   Less than 50 scales along the
    lateral line.   Pharyngeal teeth in two rows (fig. 28*e*)—

Gobio gobio
Gudgeon (fig. 32)

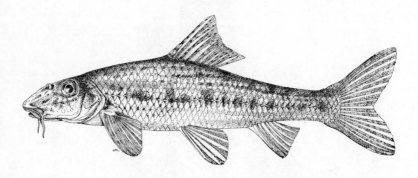

Fig. 32.   *Gobio gobio,* Gudgeon.

5 (1) Less than 15 rays in the anal fin—   6

—   More than 15 rays in the anal fin—   14

6   More than 14 rays in the dorsal fin.   Less than 35 scales along
    the lateral line.   Pharyngeal teeth: 4.4 (figs. 28*b, c*)—   7

—   Less than 12 rays in the dorsal fin.   More than 35 scales along
    the lateral line.   Pharyngeal teeth other than 4.4—   8

7 More than 31 scales along the lateral line. Less than 34 gill rakers on the first gill arch. First dorsal ray feeble, weakly serrated. Dorsal fin convex— **Carassius carassius** Crucian carp (fig. 33)

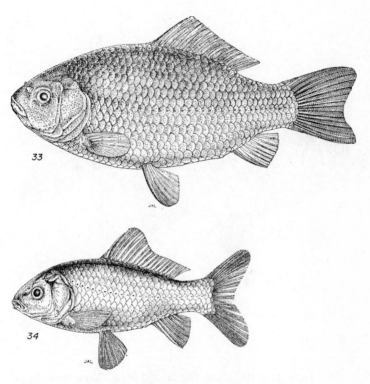

Fig. 33. *Carassius carassius*, Crucian carp.
Fig. 34. *Carassius auratus*, Goldfish.

— Less than 31 scales along the lateral line. More than 34 gill rakers on the first gill arch. First dorsal ray strong, coarsely serrated. Dorsal fin concave— **Carassius auratus** Goldfish (fig. 34)

8 (6) Less than 39 scales along the lateral series. Less than 14
rays in the pectoral fin.   Lateral line short, confined to the first
6 scales—   **Rhodeus sericeus**
                                                Bitterling (fig. 35)

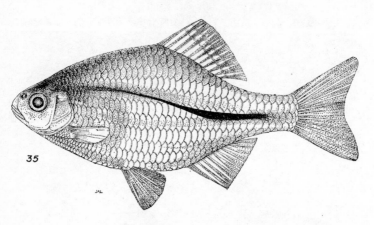

Fig. 35.   *Rhodeus sericeus,* Bitterling.

—   More than 39 scales along the lateral line.   More than 14 rays
in the pectoral fin.   Lateral line extending at least to the
middle of the body, and usually to the tail—   9

9 More than 80 scales along the lateral line, which is usually incomplete behind the middle of the body. Tubules of the lateral line extending to the free edge of the scales—

Phoxinus phoxinus
Minnow (fig. 36)

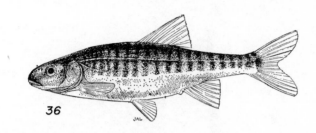

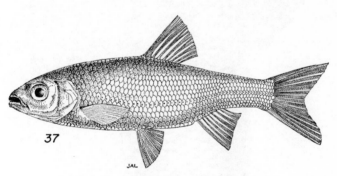

Fig. 36. *Phoxinus phoxinus*, Minnow.
Fig. 37. *Leuciscus idus*, Orfe.

— Less than 60 scales along the lateral line, which is always complete. Tubules of the lateral line not extending to the free edge of the scales— **10**

10 More than 54 scales along the lateral line; 9–10 scales between the dorsal fin and the lateral line; 5–6 scales between the anal fin and the lateral line— **Leuciscus idus**
Orfe (fig. 37)

Fig. 38. *Leuciscus cephalus*, Chub.

— Less than 54 scales along the lateral line; 7–8 scales between the dorsal fin and the lateral line; 3–4 scales between the anal fin and the lateral line—   11

11 Less than 13 rays in the anal fin. Length of the body more than 3·5 times its maximum depth. 44–53 scales along the lateral line. Pharyngeal teeth: 2.5:5.2 (figs. 28*n*, *p*)—   12

— More than 11 rays in the anal fin. Length of the body less than 3·5 times its maximum depth. 40–45 scales along the lateral line. Pharyngeal teeth not 2.5:5.2—   13

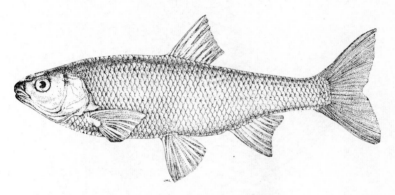

Fig. 39. *Leuciscus leuciscus,* Dace.

12 Less than 47 scales along the lateral line. Anal and dorsal fins straight or slightly convex. Fork to the caudal fin shallow—
Leuciscus cephalus
Chub (fig. 38)

— More than 46 scales along the lateral line. Anal and dorsal fins concave. Fork to the caudal fin deep— **Leuciscus leuciscus**
Dace (fig. 39)

13 (11) Scales along the lateral line 42–45. Front of the dorsal fin above or very slightly behind the base of the pelvic fins. One row of pharyngeal teeth (5:5 or 6:6) on which pectination is weak or absent (fig. 28*m*)—   **Rutilus rutilus**
Roach (fig. 40)

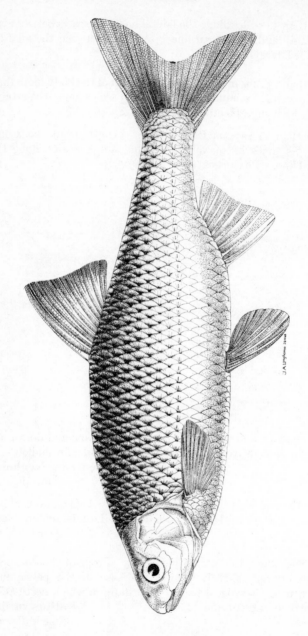

Fig. 40. *Rutilus rutilus*, Roach.

— Scales along the lateral line 40–43. Front of the dorsal fin distinctly behind the base of the pelvics. Two rows of pharyngeal teeth (3.5:5.3) on which the pectination is strong (fig. 28*l*)— **Scardinius erythrophthalmus**
Rudd (fig. 41)

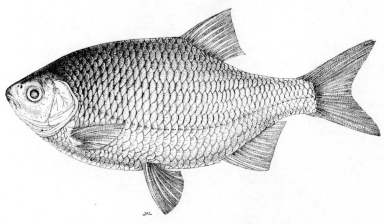

Fig. 41. *Scardinius erythrophthalmus*, Rudd.

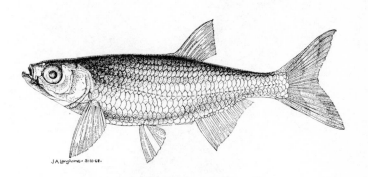

Fig. 42. *Alburnus alburnus*, Bleak.

14 (5) Length of body more than four times its maximum depth. 20–23 rays in the anal fin. Less than 5 scales between the anal fin and the lateral line— **Alburnus alburnus**
Bleak (fig. 42)

Fig. 43. *Blicca bjoerkna*, Silver bream.

— Length of body less than 3 times its maximum depth. 22–31 rays in the anal fin. More than 4 scales between the anal fin and the lateral line— **15**

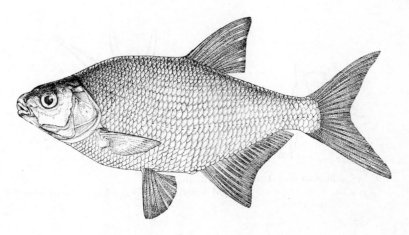

Fig. 44. *Abramis brama,* Common bream.

15 Less than 50 scales along the lateral line. Less than 27 rays in the anal fin. 8–11 scales between the dorsal fin and the lateral line. Distance between tip of snout and eye usually less than or equal to the diameter of the eye—

Blicca bjoerkna
Silver bream (fig. 43)

— More than 49 scales along the lateral line. More than 25 rays in the anal fin. 11–15 scales between the dorsal fin and the lateral line. Distance between tip of snout and eye usually more than the diameter of the eye—   **Abramis brama**
Common bream (fig. 44)

Family COBITIDAE

1   A bifid spine present in a pocket under each eye.   Less than 9
rays in the pectoral fins.   Barbels similar, all short (fig. 45*a*)—
Cobitis taenia
Spined loach (fig. 46)

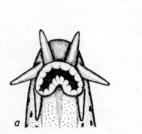 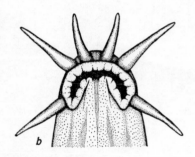

Fig. 45.   Mouth structure of Cobitidae:
a, Cobitis taenia, Spined loach;   *b, Noemacheilus barbatulus,*
Stone loach.

—   Bifid spines absent.   More than 11 rays in the pectoral fins.
Barbels long, one pair slightly longer than the others (fig. 45*b*)—
Noemacheilus barbatulus
Stone loach (fig. 47)

Family GADIDAE

One British freshwater species, **Lota lota,** Burbot (fig. 48).

Family COTTIDAE

One British freshwater species, **Cottus gobio,** Bullhead (fig. 49).

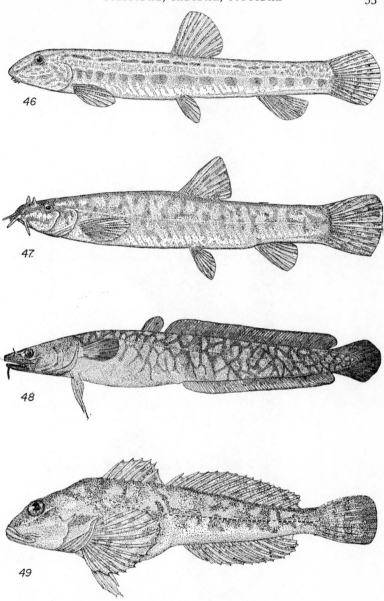

Fig. 46.   *Cobitis taenia,* Spined loach (after Demoll & Maier, 1962).
Fig. 47.   *Noemacheilus barbatulus,* Stone loach (after Demoll & Maier, 1962).
Fig. 48.   *Lota lota,* Burbot.
Fig. 49.   *Cottus gobio,* Bullhead (after Spillman, 1961).

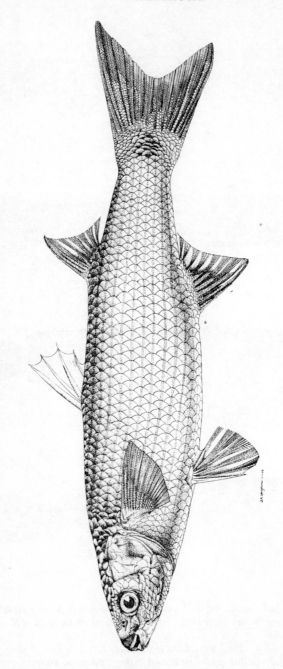

Fig. 50. *Crenimugil labrosus*, Thick-lipped mullet.

Family MUGILIDAE

1 Upper lip thick; its depth greater than a tenth of the head length and more than half the diameter of the eye. No scales present on the lower jaw— **Crenimugil labrosus**
Thick-lipped mullet (fig. 50)

— Upper lip thinner; its depth less than a tenth of the head length and less than half the diameter of the eye. Scales present on the lower jaw— **2**

2 Scales on the dorsal side of the head extending to the nostrils or beyond. Posterior edge of the preorbital bone rounded or truncated vertically— **Chelon ramada**
Thin-lipped mullet (fig. 51)

— Scales on the dorsal side of the head not extending to the nostrils. Posterior edge of the preorbital bone truncated obliquely— **Chelon auratus**
Golden mullet (fig. 52)

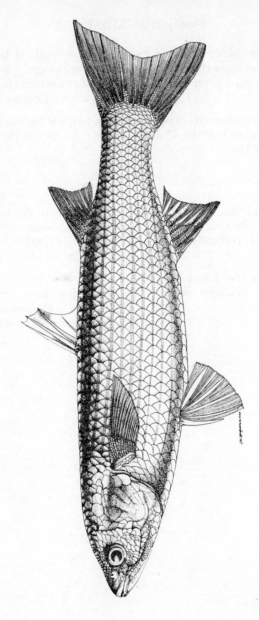

Fig. 51. *Chelon ramada*, Thin-lipped mullet.

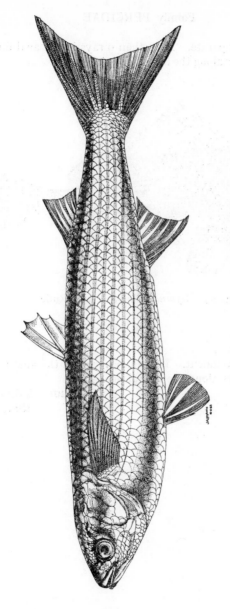

Fig. 52. *Chelon auratus*, Golden mullet.

Family PERCIDAE

1   Dorsal fins separate. More than 9 rays in the anal fin. More
than 50 scales along the lateral line—   **2**

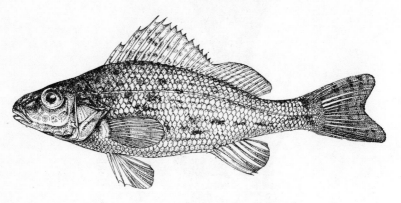

Fig. 53. *Gymnocephalus cernua*, Ruffe.

—   Dorsal fins confluent. Less than 9 rays in the anal fin. Less
than 50 scales along the lateral line—

Gymnocephalus cernua
Ruffe (fig. 53)

2   Base of the first dorsal fin longer than that of the second.   Less than 70 scales along the lateral line.   Short teeth only in the mouth—   **Perca fluviatilis**

Perch (fig. 54)

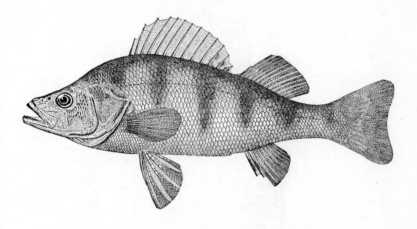

Fig. 54.   *Perca fluviatilis*, Perch.

—   Base of the first dorsal fin the same length as or shorter than that of the second.   More than 70 scales along the lateral line. Both long and short teeth present in the mouth—

                                Stizostedion lucioperca

Pikeperch, zander (fig. 55)

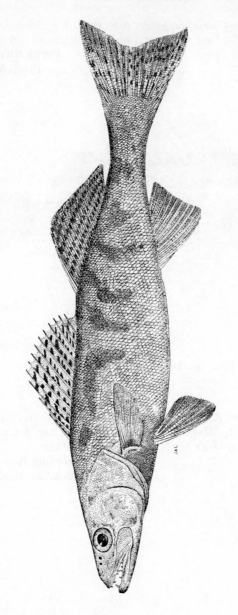

Fig. 55. *Stizostedion lucioperca*, Pikeperch, zander.

Family GOBIIDAE

One British freshwater species, **Pomatoschistus microps,**
Common goby (fig. 56).   (Several other species occur irregularly in
brackish water.)

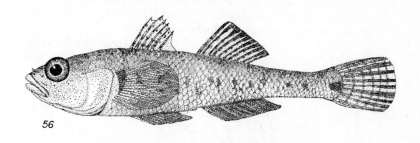

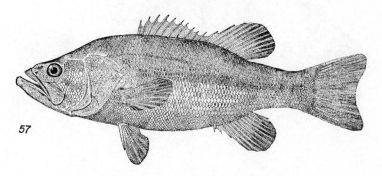

Fig. 56.   *Pomatoschistus microps,* Common goby.
Fig. 57.   *Micropterus salmoides,* Largemouth bass.

Family CENTRARCHIDAE

1   More than 50 scales along the lateral line.   Dorsal fins almost
separated by a notch.   Length of the body more than 3 times
its greatest depth—   **Micropterus salmoides**
Largemouth bass (fig. 57)

— Less than 50 scales along the lateral line. Dorsal fins continuous. Length of the body less than 3 times its greatest depth—   **2**

2 Less than 4 spines in the anal fin. Operculum ending in a convex flap which is black in colour. Gill rakers short, the longest shorter than the diameter of the eye—

Lepomis gibbosus
Pumpkinseed (fig. 58)

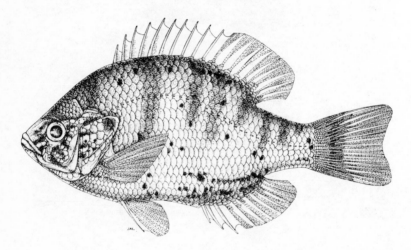

Fig. 58. *Lepomis gibbosus*, Pumpkinseed.

— More than 4 spines in the anal fin. Operculum ending in two flat points, neither of which is black in colour. Gill rakers long, the longest longer than the diameter of the eye—

Ambloplites rupestris
Rock bass (fig. 59)

Family SERRANIDAE

One British freshwater species, **Dicentrarchus labrax,** Sea bass (fig. 60).

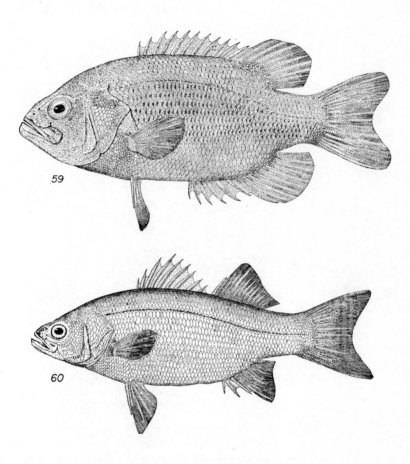

Fig. 59.   *Ambloplites rupestris,* Rock bass.
Fig. 60.   *Dicentrarchus labrax,* Sea bass.

Family GASTEROSTEIDAE

1   Less than 5 dorsal spines (normally 3), the longest about same height as the dorsal fin. Gill openings narrow, restricted to the sides. Throat of the male vivid red during the breeding season—   **Gasterosteus aculeatus**

Three-spined stickleback (fig. 61)

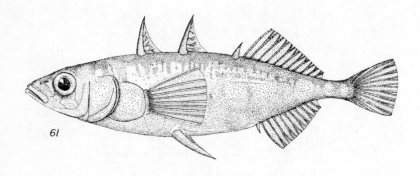

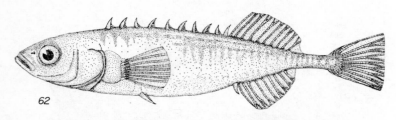

Fig. 61.   *Gasterosteus aculeatus,* Three-spined stickleback.
Fig. 62.   *Pungitius pungitius,* Ten-spined stickleback.

—   More than 6 dorsal spines (normally 10), the longest only about half the height of the dorsal fin. Gill openings wide, confluent ventrally. Throat of the male vivid black during the breeding season—   **Pungitius pungitius**

Ten-spined stickleback (fig. 62)

Family PLEURONECTIDAE

One British freshwater species, **Platichthys flesus,** Flounder (fig. 63). (Other species occur irregularly in brackish water.)

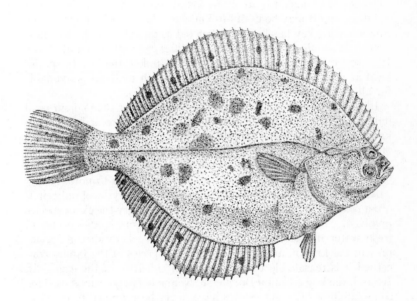

Fig. 63. *Platichthys flesus,* Flounder.

PRELIMINARY KEY
TO FISH EGGS BY FAMILIES

The eggs of various fish are often found during work in freshwater habitats, and it may be useful to know to which species they belong. The following key has been constructed as an aid in such identifications. It should be noted that it identifies eggs only to family level. It is hoped that it may be possible to complete the key to species level at a later date, when sufficient research material is available for all the species concerned in the British Isles.

Ideally, eggs should be examined when fresh, for their colour is an important character in identification. Furthermore, it is useful to know exactly where and when they were collected, as both the site of laying and the time of year are relevant and used in the key below. The attachment relationships of the eggs to each other and to weeds or other substrata are also relevant characteristics to note.

Although this key allows identification to family level only, it is often possible to conclude with reasonable certainty the exact species involved. Thus for seven of the families, only one species occurs in fresh water in the British Isles. In waters where all the species present are known, and there is only one species of the family concerned it is reasonable to assume specific identity of the eggs. In Ireland, the key given by Bracken & Kennedy (1967) can be used for some families. Certain species have never been known to breed in the British Isles (e.g. *Acipenser sturio* and *Coregonus oxyrinchus*).

1   Eggs found only in the sea—   ANGUILLIDAE
                                                    MUGILIDAE
                                                    GOBIIDAE
                                                    SERRANIDAE
                                                    PLEURONECTIDAE

—   Eggs found in fresh or brackish waters—   2

2 Eggs single, or occasionally in small clumps of variable number (usually less than ten)— 3

— Eggs in definite clumps or ribbons (usually more than 50 in each)— **16**

3 Eggs loose, slightly buoyant, usually in or near estuaries. (Diameter of eggs 4–5 mm. Occurring from May to June)—
CLUPEIDAE

— Eggs not loose and buoyant— 4

4 Eggs not adhesive or only weakly so. Usually found (often buried) among coarse gravels in well oxygenated places; normally in running water or at the edges of clean lakes— 5

— Eggs adhesive. Usually found attached to weed or stones (never buried) in a variety of habitats— 8

5 Eggs less than 1·5 mm diameter, white in colour. (Eggs buried under small stones in running water. Occurring from March to May)—
PETROMYZONIDAE

— Eggs more than 1·5 mm diameter, yellow-orange in colour— 6

6 Eggs less than 3 mm diameter. (Eggs found among coarse gravel and stones in standing water. Occurring from December to February)—
COREGONIDAE

— Eggs more than 3 mm diameter— 7

7 Eggs less than 4 mm diameter. (Eggs found buried among coarse gravel in running water. Occurring from March to May)—
THYMALLIDAE

— Eggs more than 4 mm diameter—
SALMONIDAE

8 (4) Eggs more than 2 mm diameter— 9

— Eggs less than 2 mm diameter— **13**

9 A nest or protection of some kind sheltering the eggs— **10**

—   No nest nor protection sheltering eggs—   **11**

10   Eggs found within freshwater mussels (Unionidae). (Eggs
yellow in colour. Occurring from May to July)—
CYPRINIDAE (*Rhodeus* only)

—   Eggs not found within freshwater mussels. (Eggs yellow in
colour, laid in a circular depression in the substratum.
Occurring from April to August)—   CENTRARCHIDAE

11 (9) Eggs grey, less than 2·5 mm diameter, attached to stones in
rivers where the current is strong. (Eggs occurring from April
to July)—   ACIPENSERIDAE

—   Eggs not grey, more than 2·5 mm diameter, found attached to
weed in lakes and slow-flowing rivers—   **12**

12   Eggs pale yellow, occurring from May to June—   SILURIDAE

—   Eggs brown, occurring from February to May—   ESOCIDAE

13 (8) Eggs found from January to February. (Diameter 0·8–
1·5 mm, attached to plants and stones)—   GADIDAE

—   Eggs found from March to September—   **14**

14   Eggs less than 1·2 mm diameter, rarely found in standing
water—   **15**

—   Eggs more than 1·2 mm diameter, often found in standing
water—   CYPRINIDAE (Except *Rhodeus*)

15   Eggs found in or near estuaries, from March to April. (Eggs
yellow in colour; attached to plants and stones)—
OSMERIDAE

—   Eggs found in fresh water only, from April to June. (Eggs
yellow in colour; attached to plants and stones)—   COBITIDAE

16 (2) Eggs white or whitish yellow, laid in ribbons among weed, etc. or as a single large clump at the base of weeds—

PERCIDAE

—   Eggs yellow, laid in small clumps—   17

17   Eggs more than 2 mm diameter, laid in a single mass (usually more than 1 cm across) adhering to the under-surfaces of stones. (Eggs occurring from February to May, usually in streams)—

COTTIDAE

—   Eggs less than 2 mm diameter, laid in a single mass (usually less than 1 cm across) inside a small nest built of pieces of vegetation. (Eggs occurring from March to June)— GASTEROSTEIDAE

PRELIMINARY KEY
TO FISH LARVAE
BY FAMILIES

The main developmental stages found in freshwater fishes in the British Isles are as follows: (1) Egg; after fertilisation this develops a secondary membrane. (2) Larva; the stage between hatching from the egg and final absorption of the yolk sac. (3) Post Larva; the stage between final absorption of the yolk sac and the completion of fin definition. (4) Fry; the stage between the completion of fin definition and the attainment of adult characteristics. (5) Adult.

Although it has been possible to define these stages more or less exactly, it should be noted that there is a gradual transition from fertilised egg to adult and a variety of intermediate stages are found. Thus Balinsky (1948) defined more than forty different stages between the fertilised egg and fry stages in the British Cyprinidae. The key given below has been developed for post larvae, i.e. for a stage between fertilised egg and adult, keys for both of which have already been given. As with the key to eggs, that below identifies post larvae to family level only; it is hoped that it may be possible to complete the key to species level at a later date when sufficient research material is available.

As with the keys to eggs and scales, however, it is often possible to identify the exact species involved after the family has been ascertained. Thus with seven of the families involved only one species occurs in fresh water in the British Isles. A key to all the species of Cyprinidae has been given by Balinsky (1948) while for Irish waters the key for coarse fish published by Bracken & Kennedy (1967) can be used for some species.

1 Found only in the sea—

ANGUILLIDAE
MUGILIDAE
GOBIIDAE
SERRANIDAE
PLEURONECTIDAE

70

— Found in fresh or brackish waters—   **2**

2 No paired fins or lower jaw present. Seven pairs of gill
openings. Usually found buried in sand in running water—
PETROMYZONIDAE

— Both paired fins and lower jaw present. One pair of gill
openings each protected by an operculum—   **3**

3 Distinct barbels present near mouth—   **4**

— Distinct barbels absent—   **5**

4 Barbels anterior to mouth. Obvious snout present—
ACIPENSERIDAE

— Barbels posterior to mouth. Obvious snout absent—
SILURIDAE

5 (3) Length of post larva more than 12·5 mm—   **6**

— Length of post larva less than 12·5 mm—   **9**

6 Dark stripe through eye. Tail pointed at end— ESOCIDAE

— No dark stripe through eye. Tail rounded or concave at
end—   **7**

7 Anus opening nearer tail than middle of body. Occurring
mainly in estuaries—   CLUPEIDAE

— Anus opening nearer middle of body than tail—   **8**

8 Length of post larva more than 20 mm—   SALMONIDAE

— Length of post larva less than 20 mm—   THYMALLIDAE

9 (5) Anus opening nearer anterior than posterior end of body—
GADIDAE

— Anus opening midway or nearer posterior than anterior end of
body—   **10**

10 Swim bladder small or absent, its maximum length never greater than that of eye—   16

— Swim bladder larger, its length usually about twice that of eye—   11

11 Fine black marks on edges of myotomes—   PERCIDAE

— No fine black marks on edges of myotomes—   12

12 Anus opening about midway along body—
                                                    CENTRARCHIDAE

— Anus opening in posterior half of body—   13

13 Pigment cells scattered over most of body—
                                                    GASTEROSTEIDAE

— Pigment cells confined to specific parts of body, often in linear series—   14

14 Eyes large, more than half length of head—   15

— Eyes small, less than half length of head—   CYPRINIDAE

15 Length of post larva more than 8 mm. Pigment cells in a double row down back and round gut—   COREGONIDAE

— Length of post larva less than 8 mm. Pigment cells not in this pattern—   OSMERIDAE

16 (10) Length of post larva less than 9 mm. Pectoral fins longer than broad. Underside of head with numerous wart-like growths—   COBITIDAE

— Length of post larva more than 9 mm. Pectoral fins broader than long. Underside of head smooth—   COTTIDAE

PRELIMINARY KEY
TO FISH SCALES
BY FAMILIES

As with their eggs, the scales of fish are often found during work in aquatic habitats and in some situations (e.g. fish stomachs, birds, nests, sediments, etc.) they may be the only part of the fish left intact. It is clearly useful from the ecological viewpoint to be able to identify such scales, and the following key is a preliminary one which allows the identification to family level of the scales of freshwater fish occurring in the British Isles. It is hoped that a complete account and a key to species level will be published at

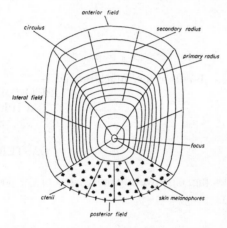

Fig. 64.   General characteristics of fish scales.   The area exposed in life is indicated by pigment cells (mélanophores) present in the overlying skin.

a later date, when sufficient research material is available.

This key should be used with caution, and it is advisable to have several scales available for any one identification. The characters referred to in the key are indicated in fig. 64. For examination, scales should be mounted as described in the section dealing with

73

collection and preservation (p. 8). As is apparent from the key to adult fish, several freshwater species occurring in the British Isles have no scales. In those which do possess scales there are normally differences between scales from different parts of the body — those from the head region, the lateral line and adjacent to the fins normally showing some modification of shape. The key below refers to typical body scales (always the great majority) from each of the families concerned, found above and below the lateral line between the head and the tail. As with eggs, although the identification is only to family level, it is often possible to conclude with reasonable certainty the exact species involved. Thus for eight of the families involved only one species occurs in fresh water in the British Isles, and where other families are involved only one species may be present in the habitat concerned.

1　True scales absent or very much modified—
　　　　　　　　　　　　　　　PETROMYZONIDAE
　　　　　　　　　　　　　　　ACIPENSERIDAE
　　　　　　　　　　　　　　　SILURIDAE
　　　　　　　　　　　　　　　COTTIDAE
　　　　　　　　　　　　　GASTEROSTEIDAE

—　True scales (fig. 64) covering most parts of the body (except in young fry)—　　　　　　　　　　　　　　　　　　　2

2　Scales cycloid in character (plate I*a*)—　　　　　　　3
—　Scales ctenoid in character (plate I*b*)—　　　　　　12

3　Radii essentially transverse. Circuli also more or less transverse—　　　　　　　　　　　　　　　　CLUPEIDAE
—　Radii, when present, essentially radiating from focus. Circuli never transverse—　　　　　　　　　　　　　　　4

4　Primary radii absent—　　　　　　　　　　　　　　5
—　Primary radii present—　　　　　　　　　　　　　10

PLATE I

Typical scales from two contrasting species: above, cycloid type from the whitefish, *Coregonus lavaretus;* below, ctenoid type from the perch, *Perca fluviatilis*.

5 Circuli normal.   Scale not greatly elongate—   **6**

— Circuli abnormal, modified to give a beaded appearance.   Scale always greatly elongate—   ANGUILLIDAE

6 Scale never circular.   Circuli never exactly concentric—   **7**

— Scale circular.   Circuli normally exactly concentric—
                                                    GADIDAE

7 Radii absent.   Circuli not marking scale into four primary fields—   **8**

— Secondary radii often present, usually in posterior field.   Circuli spaced and angulated to divide scale into four primary fields— **9**

8 Focus of scale defined, more or less central, and usually longitudinally ovoid.   Scale normally longer than wide—
                                                    SALMONIDAE

— Focus of scale poorly defined, displaced towards the anterior margin, and usually transversely ovoid.   Scale normally wider than long—   OSMERIDAE

9 Anterior edge and parts of circuli in anterior field of scale with three or more well marked ridges—   THYMALLIDAE

— Anterior edge and parts of circuli in anterior field of scale without well marked ridges—   COREGONIDAE

10 (4) Primary radii found only in anterior field—   ESOCIDAE

— Primary radii found in posterior field and usually elsewhere also—   **11**

11 Scale usually sub-quadrate in shape, never a rounded oval. Primary radii usually found in both anterior and posterior fields, but never in lateral fields.   Scales usually large (more than 1 mm in diameter)—   CYPRINIDAE

— Scale a rounded oval in shape.   Primary radii present in all fields. Scales always very small (less than 1 mm in diameter)—   COBITIDAE

12 (2) Ctenii always present.   Scale more or less symmetrical, rarely longer than broad—   **13**

— Ctenii usually absent.   Scale often asymmetrical, and often longer than broad—   PLEURONECTIDAE

13 Ctenii occurring only in marginal row, persisting elsewhere in posterior field as basal segments of previous ctenii—   **14**

— Ctenii occurring over much of posterior field—
                                                  CENTRARCHIDAE

14 Anterior edge of scale conspicuously lobed—   PERCIDAE

— Anterior edge of scale not conspicuously lobed—   **15**

15 Scale much wider than long.   Front margin of scale rounded. Ctenii relatively long, usually more than one twentieth of length of scale—   GOBIIDAE

— Scale about as wide as long.   Front margin of scale with well defined corners.   Ctenii relatively short, usually less than one fiftieth of length of scale—   **16**

16 Anterior corners of scale acute.   Anterior field with many primary and secondary radii—   SERRANIDAE

— Anterior corners of scale obtuse.   Anterior field with few primary and secondary radii—   MUGILIDAE

DISTRIBUTION AND ECOLOGY

The maps shown on the following pages represent the information so far ingathered from a project to record the distribution of freshwater fishes in the British Isles. This scheme was started in 1966 and is still in progress; thus the data shown must be regarded as being of a preliminary nature. Nevertheless, sufficient records are available from enough parts of the British Isles to make these maps meaningful in a general way, and of value in conjunction with the key. A preliminary account of this mapping scheme has been published elsewhere (Maitland, 1969).

The maps indicate by a symbol the presence of each species in every 10-kilometre square of the Ordnance Survey National Grid in which it occurs. The large squares shown on the following maps are the 100-kilometre squares; the 10-kilometre squares are shown on the $\frac{1}{4}$-inch and 1 inch Ordnance maps; the latter also show the 1-kilometre squares. These maps have been reproduced the same size as those in the *Atlas of the British flora* (Perring & Walters, 1962) and the transparent overlays (showing rivers, altitude, geology, rainfall, humidity and temperature) included in that work fit the present maps also.

Much further information is required for all species, and any records concerning parts of the British Isles not yet covered would be of great value to the scheme. In the maps which follow, symbols have been used to indicate different types of record: authentic post-1960 records (●); authentic pre-1960 records (o); presumed extinct localities (×). As a study of the above key and figures will show, some species of fish are much easier to identify accurately than others. For record purposes the species fall into three categories: (a) easily recognised species which do not require additional verification, (b) less easily recognised species which require additional verification (such species are denoted below by a single asterisk after the common name), (c) difficult or very rare species whose identification must be verified by a specialist (such species are denoted below by a double asterisk after the common name). Anyone interested in fish who has authentic records of any species in a square not included in the following maps is requested to send these to the author. All specimens of uncommon (*) or rare (**) species must be verified by a recognised authority, the local Fisheries Officer (or his equivalent) in the case of the former category, the author or the British Museum (Mr A. C. Wheeler) for either.

In the notes on ecology which accompany the maps, only the basic details about each species have been given, in a rather abbreviated manner. The information refers to the average conditions or measurements (so far as they are known) within the British Isles, not their extremes.

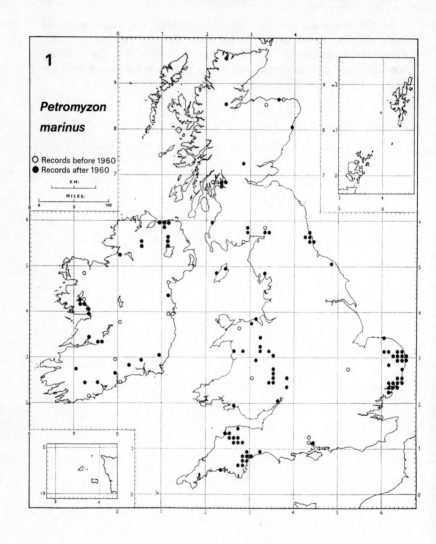

1. *Petromyzon marinus*, Sea lamprey

   Indigenous, fairly widespread and common; anadromous.   Estuaries and easily accessible rivers.   Adult length 60–90 cm.   Breeds March-May.   Clear eggs (1·2 mm) in nests among stones in running water. Food filtered organic material when larvae, fish when adult.

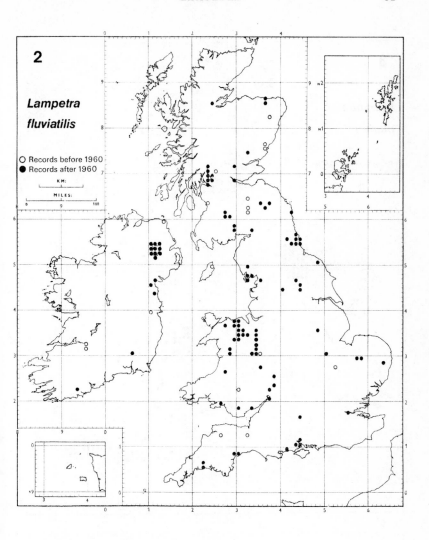

2. *Lampetra fluviatilis*, River lamprey**

Indigenous, fairly widespread and common; anadromous. Estuaries and easily accessible lakes, rivers and streams. Adult length 30–50 cm. Breeds April-May. Clear eggs (1 mm) in nests among stones in running water. Food filtered organic material when larvae, fish when adult.

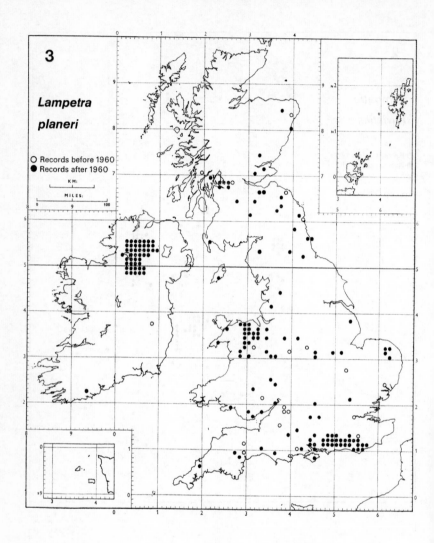

3. *Lampetra planeri*, Brook lamprey**

Indigenous, fairly widespread and common. Sandy and gravelly rivers and streams. Adult length 13–25 cm. Breeds April-June. Clear eggs (0·9 mm) in nests among stones in running water. Food filtered organic material when larvae, do not feed as adults.

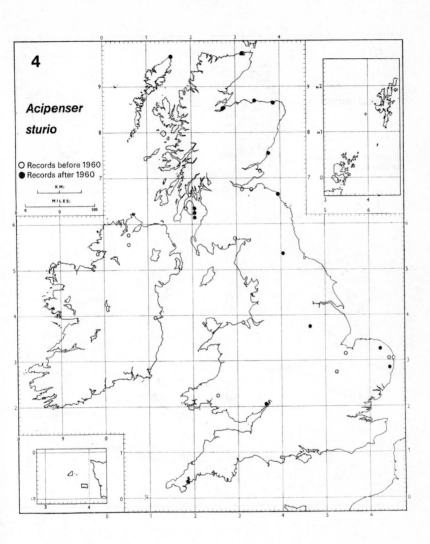

4. *Acipenser sturio*, Sturgeon

    Indigenous, widespread but rare; anadromous.   Vagrant in estuaries.
Adult length 150–250 cm.   Breeds April-July but has never been
known to do so in the British Isles.   Grey eggs (2·3 mm) attached to
stones in running water.   Food benthic invertebrates.

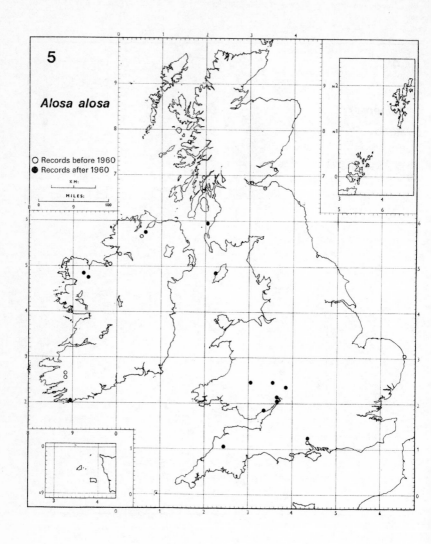

5. *Alosa alosa*, Allis shad**

Indigenous, fairly local and rare; anadromous. Estuaries and lower reaches of rivers. Adult length 30–50 cm. Breeds May-June. Clear eggs (4·4 mm) laid in or near estuarine waters. Food invertebrates, especially plankton.

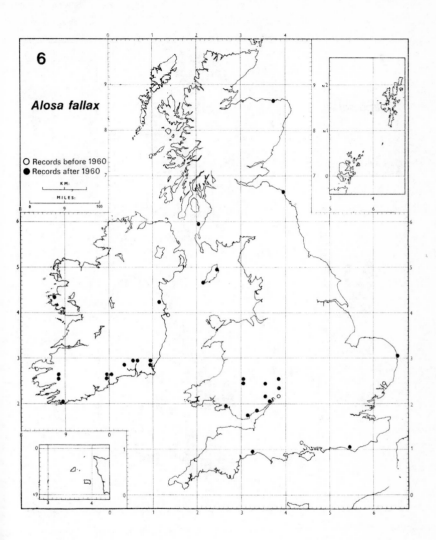

6. *Alosa fallax*, Twaite shad**

Indigenous, fairly widespread and common; anadromous. Estuaries and lower reaches of rivers. Adult length 25–40 cm. Breeds May-June. Clear eggs (4·4 mm) laid in or near estuarine waters. Food invertebrates, especially plankton.

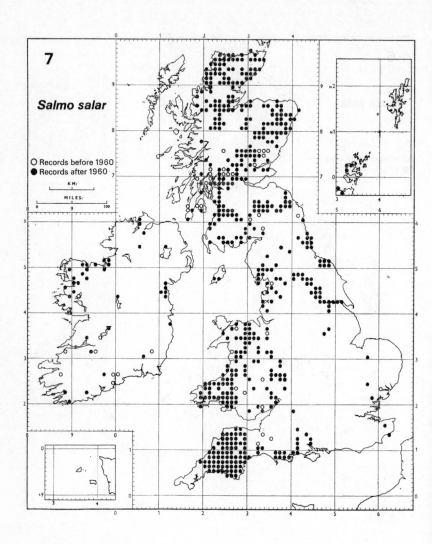

7. *Salmo salar*, Salmon.

Indigenous, widespread and common; anadromous. Clear stony rivers, streams and lakes. Adult length 40–100 cm. Breeds October-January. Orange eggs (6 mm) in redds among gravel in running water. Food invertebrates when small, invertebrates and fish when large.

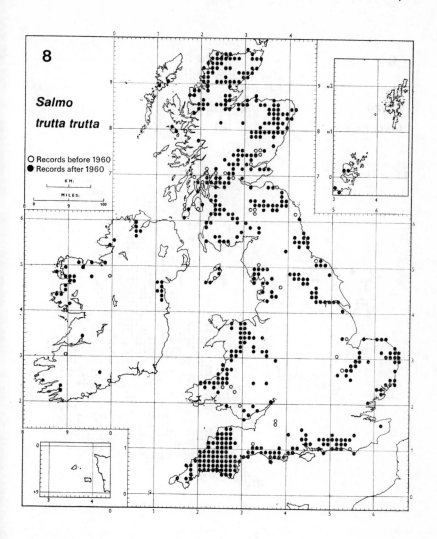

8. *Salmo trutta trutta*, Sea trout.

Indigenous, widespread and abundant; anadromous. Unpolluted estuaries, clear stony rivers, streams and lakes. Adult length 20-50 cm. Breeds October-January. Orange eggs (4 mm) in redds among gravel in running water. Food invertebrates when small; invertebrates and some fish when large.

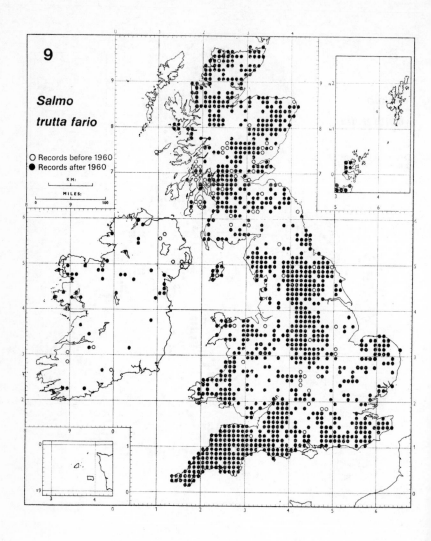

9. *Salmo trutta fario,* Brown trout.

Indigenous, widespread and abundant. Almost all types of unpolluted freshwater body where spawning grounds are available, but not too many predators. Adult length 20-50 cm. Breeds October-January. Orange eggs (4 mm) in redds among gravel in running water. Food invertebrates when small; invertebrates and fish when large.

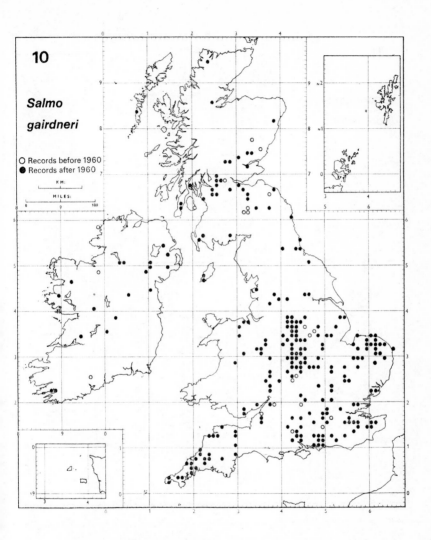

10. *Salmo gairdneri*, Rainbow trout.

Introduced, widespread and common. Clear lakes, rivers and streams. Adult length 25–45 cm. Breeds October-March but only in a few localities. Orange eggs (4 mm) in redds among gravel in running water. Food invertebrates when small, invertebrates and fish when large.

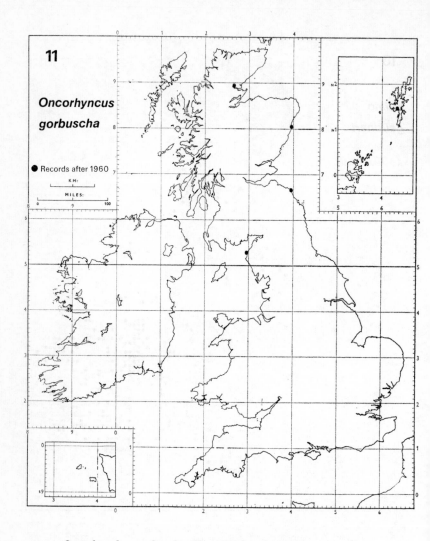

11. *Oncorhynchus gorbuscha*, Humpback salmon.**
   Introduced, occasional and rare; anadromous; vagrant.   Clear stony rivers and streams.   Adult length 40–60 cm. Breeds September-October but has never done so in the British Isles.   Orange eggs (5 mm) in redds among coarse gravel in running water.   Food invertebrates when small, invertebrates and fish when large.

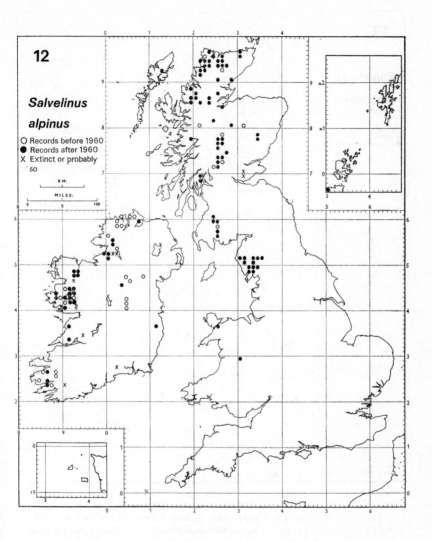

12. *Salvelinus alpinus*, Charr.

Indigenous; fairly local but common. Poor stony lakes. Adult length 20–40 cm. Breeds October-March. Yellow eggs (3·5 mm) among coarse gravel in running and standing waters. Food invertebrates, especially plankton.

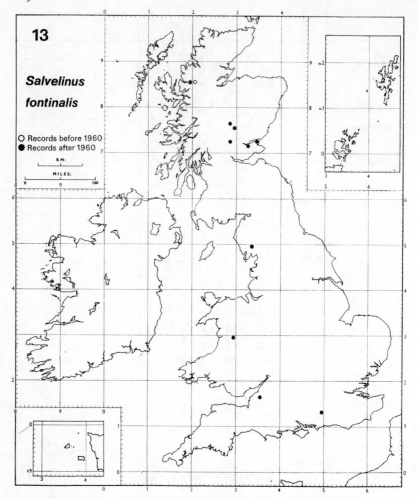

13. *Salvelinus fontinalis*, American brook trout, speckled charr.*

Introduced, very local and rare. Clear lakes, rivers and streams. Adult length 20–35 cm. Breeds October-March. Yellow eggs (3·5 mm) among coarse gravel in running and standing waters. Food invertebrates.

This fish was introduced from America, where it lives mainly in running water; there it is called "brook trout", "speckled trout" or "speckled charr". In Britain it has most commonly been called "American brook trout", but since as a *Salvelinus* it is properly a charr rather than a trout *(Salmo)*, the names "speckled charr" or "brook charr" seem preferable.

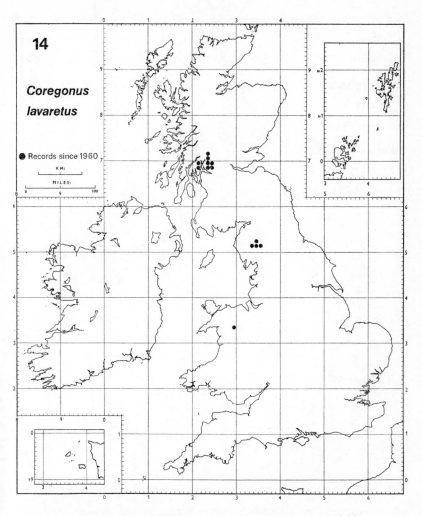

14. *Coregonus lavaretus*, Whitefish, schelly, powan, gwyniad.**

Indigenous, very local but common. Relatively large deep lakes. Adult length 20–35 cm. Breeds December-January. Yellow eggs (2·5 mm) among gravel and stones in standing water. Food invertebrates, especially plankton.

This fish has local names: schelly in the Lake District, powan in Scotland, gwyniad in Wales.

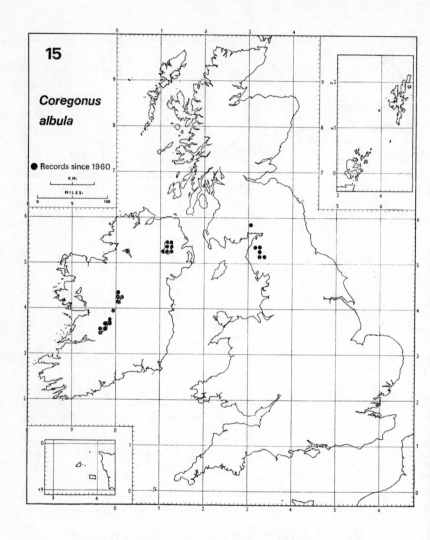

15. *Coregonus albula,* Vendace, pollan (Ireland).**

Indigenous, very local but common.   Relatively large deep lakes.
Adult length 15-25 cm.   Breeds November-December.   Yellow eggs
(2·1 mm) among gravel and stones in standing water.   Food invertebrates, especially plankton.

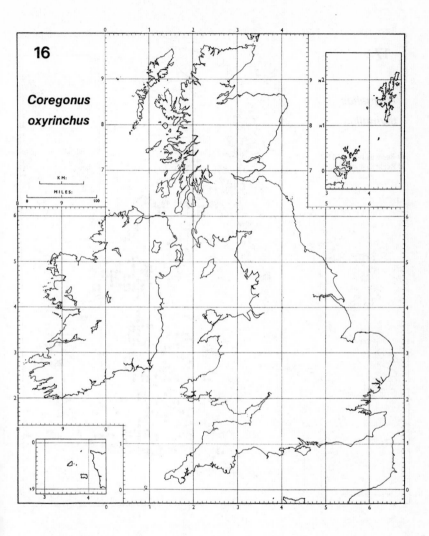

16. *Coregonus oxyrinchus*, Houting.**

Indigenous, very local and rare; anadromous; vagrant. Estuaries. Adult length 25–35 cm. Breeds December-January but has never been known to do so in the British Isles. Yellow eggs (2·9 mm) among gravel in running water. Food invertebrates, especially plankton.

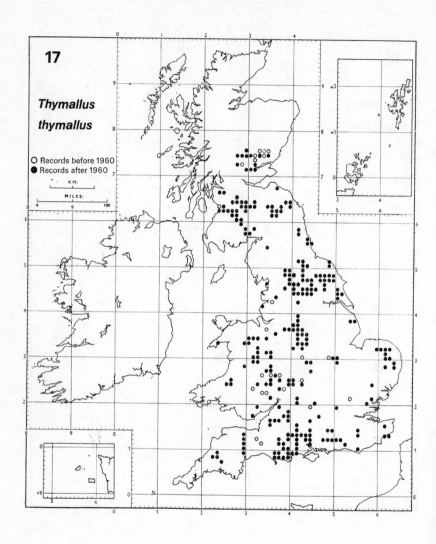

17. *Thymallus thymallus*, Grayling.

Indigenous, fairly widespread and common. Stony rivers. Adult length 20–40 cm. Breeds March-May. Yellow eggs (3·6 mm) among sand and gravel in running water. Food benthic invertebrates.

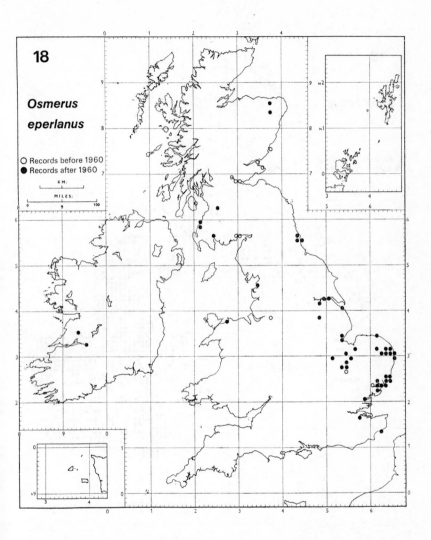

18. *Osmerus eperlanus*, Smelt.

Indigenous, fairly widespread and common; anadromous. Estuaries and lower reaches of rivers. Adult length 10–17 cm. Breeds March–April. Yellow eggs (0·9 mm) attached to weeds etc. in rivers just above estuaries. Food invertebrates when small, invertebrates and fish when large.

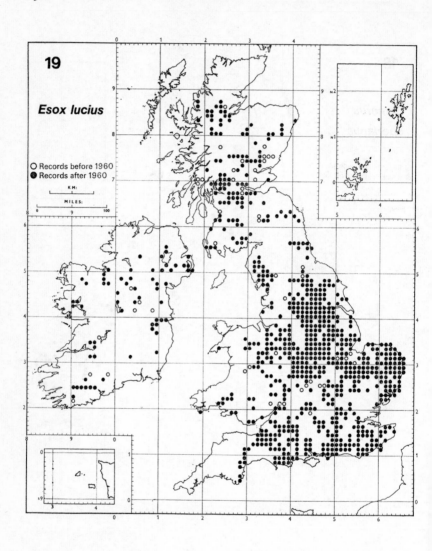

19. *Esox lucius*, Pike.

Indigenous, widespread and common. Lakes, slow flowing rivers and canals. Adult length 40–100 cm. Breeds February–May. Brown eggs (2·7 mm) attached to weeds in standing or slow-flowing water. Food invertebrates when small, fish when large.

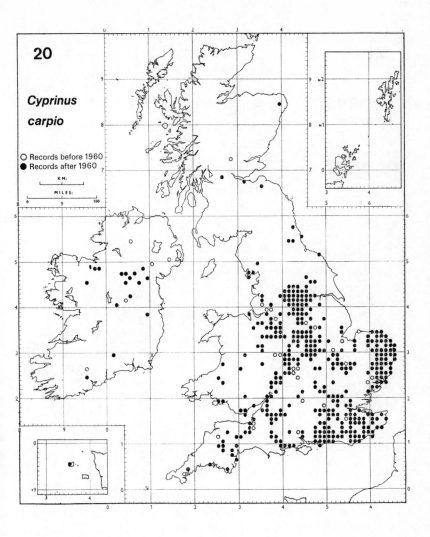

20. *Cyprinus carpio*, Carp.

Introduced, fairly widespread and common. Rich weedy lakes, canals and slow-flowing rivers. Adult length 25–50 cm. Breeds May-July. Yellow eggs (1·5 mm) attached to weeds in standing or slow-flowing water. Food invertebrates and some plants.

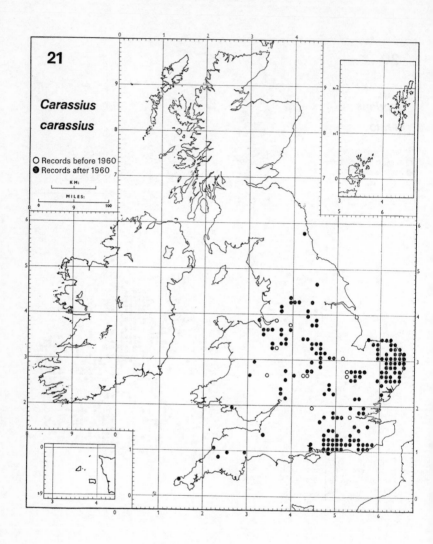

21

Carassius

carassius

O Records before 1960
● Records after 1960

KM:

MILES:

21.   *Carassius carassius*, Crucian carp.*
   Introduced, fairly local but common.   Rich weedy lakes, canals and slow-flowing rivers.   Adult length 15–25 cm.   Breeds May-June. Yellow eggs (1·5 mm) attached to weeds in standing water.   Food invertebrates and some plants.

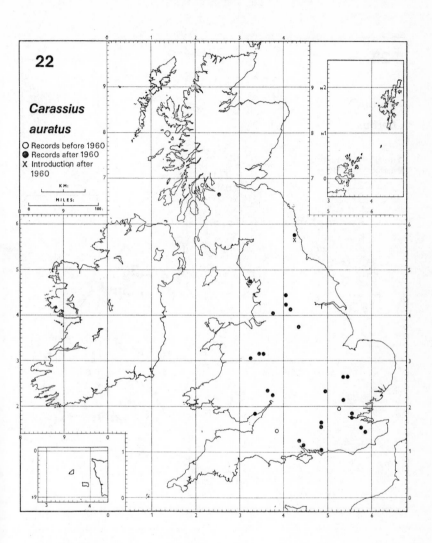

22. *Carassius auratus*, Goldfish.**

Introduced, fairly local though sometimes common. Rich weedy lakes and canals. Adult length 15–25 cm. Breeds May-July. Yellow eggs (1·5 mm) attached to weeds in standing water. Food invertebrates and some plants.

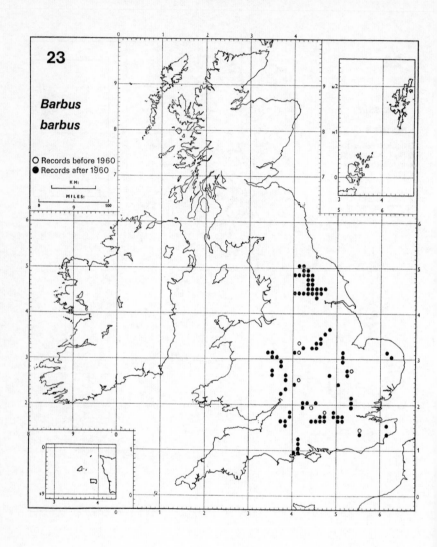

23. *Barbus barbus*, Barbel.

Indigenous, fairly local but common. Clear sandy or stony rivers. Adult length 30–50 cm. Breeds May-July. Yellow eggs (2 mm) attached to stones in running water. Food invertebrates.

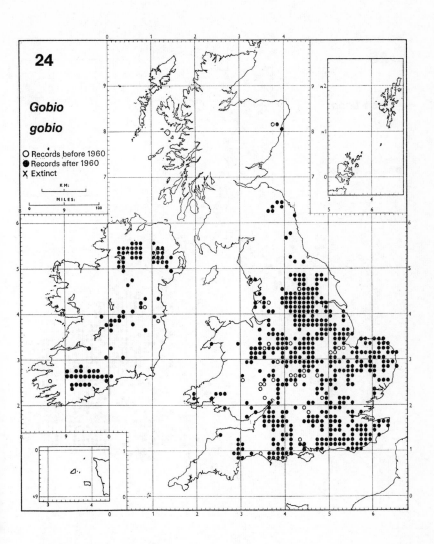

24. *Gobio gobio*, Gudgeon.

Indigenous, fairly widespread and common. Rich, sandy rivers; some lakes and canals. Adult length 10–15 cm. Breeds May-June. Yellow eggs (1·8 mm) attached to stones and weeds usually in running water. Food invertebrates and some plants.

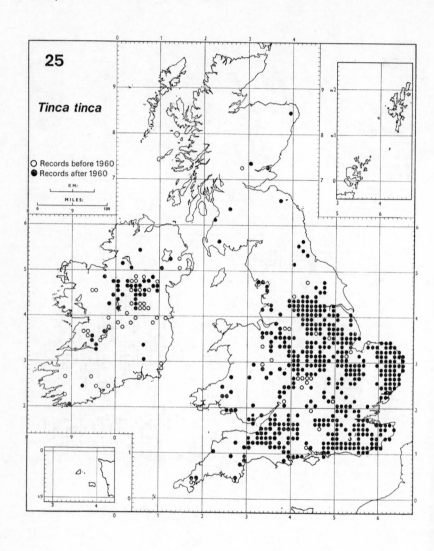

25. *Tinca tinca*, Tench.

Indigenous, fairly widespread and common. Rich weedy lakes, canals and slow-flowing rivers. Adult length 20–30 cm. Breeds May-July. Yellow eggs (1·1 mm) attached to weeds in standing or slow-flowing water. Food invertebrates and some plants.

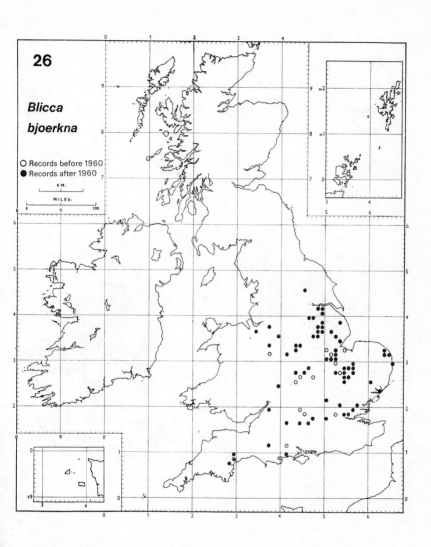

26. *Blicca bjoerkna*, Silver bream.**
   Indigenous, local but fairly common. Rich lakes, canals and slow-flowing rivers. Adult length 20–30 cm. Breeds May–July. Yellow eggs (1·9 mm) attached to weeds in standing or slow-flowing water. Food invertebrates.

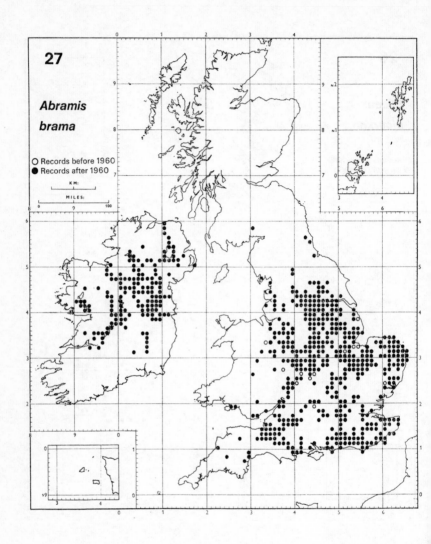

27. *Abramis brama,* Common bream.

Indigenous, fairly widespread and common. Rich lakes, canals and slow-flowing rivers. Adult length 25–45 cm. Breeds May-July. Yellow eggs (1·5 mm) attached to weeds in standing or slow-flowing water. Food invertebrates.

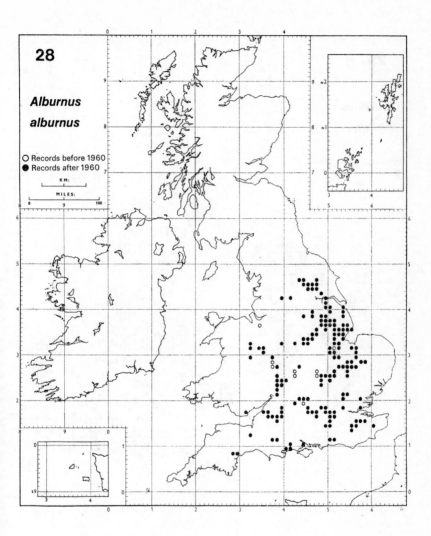

28. *Alburnus alburnus*, Bleak.

Indigenous, fairly local and common. Clear lakes and rivers. Adult length 10–15 cm. Breeds April-June. Yellow eggs (1·5 mm) attached to stones, etc. in standing or running water. Food invertebrates.

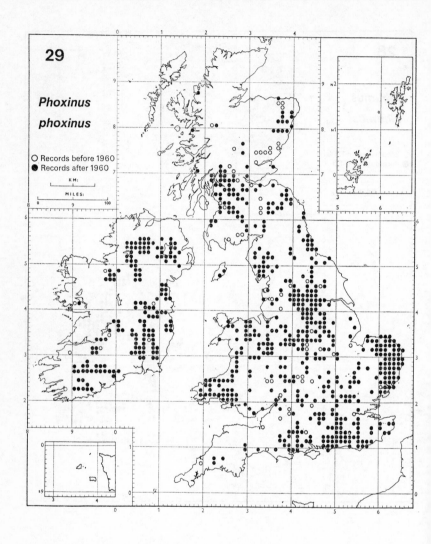

29. *Phoxinus phoxinus*, Minnow.

Indigenous, fairly widespread and common. Clear, stony lakes, rivers and streams. Adult length 6–10 cm. Breeds April-June. Yellow eggs (1·5 mm) attached to stones in running water. Food invertebrates and algae.

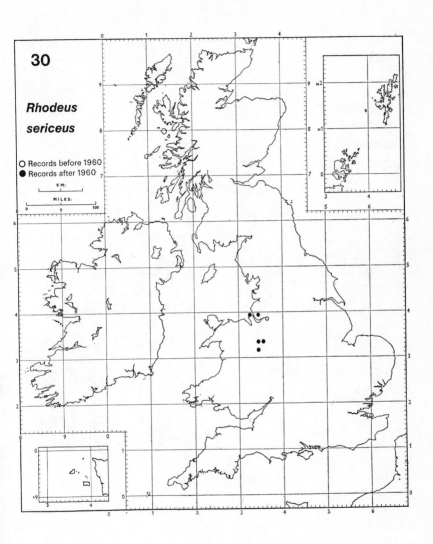

30. *Rhodeus sericeus*, Bitterling.**
    Introduced, very local and rare. Sandy lakes, canals and slow-flowing rivers. Adult length 5–8 cm. Breeds May-July. Yellow eggs (3 mm) in the mantle cavities of unionid mussels. Food invertebrates.

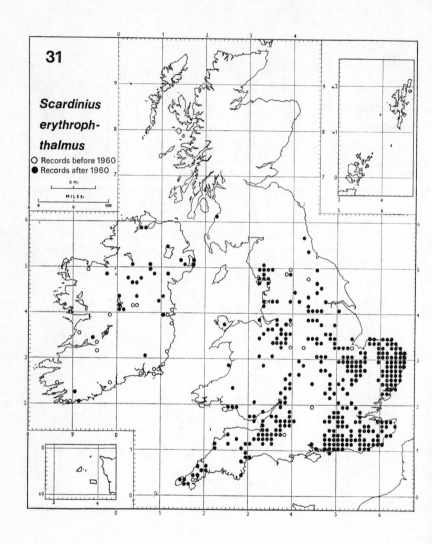

31. *Scardinius erythrophthalmus*, Rudd.

Indigenous, fairly widespread and common. Rich lakes, canals and slow-flowing rivers. Adult length 15–30 cm. Breeds April-June. Yellow eggs (1·4 mm) attached to weeds in standing or slow-flowing water. Food invertebrates and some plants.

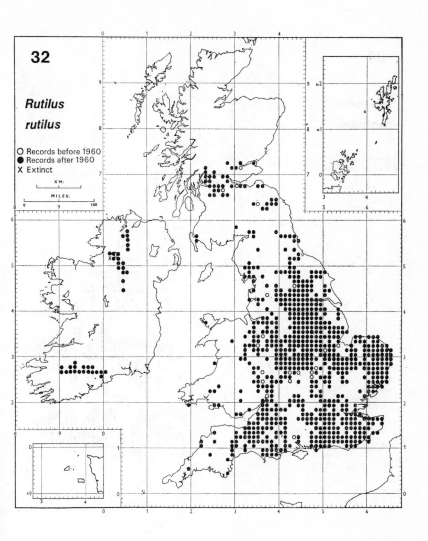

32. *Rutilus rutilus*, Roach.

Indigenous, fairly widespread and common. Rich lakes, canals and slow-flowing rivers. Adult length 15–30 cm. Breeds April-June. Yellow eggs (1·4 mm) attached to weed, etc. in standing or running water. Food invertebrates and some plants.

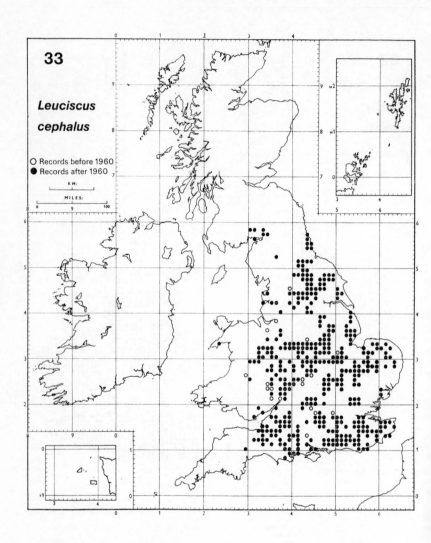

33. *Leuciscus cephalus*, Chub.

    Indigenous, fairly local but common.   Middle and lower reaches of
rivers and some lakes.   Adult length 30–45 cm.   Breeds April-June.
Yellow eggs (2 mm) attached to plants, etc. in slow-flowing water.
Food invertebrates and plants when small, invertebrates and fish when
large.

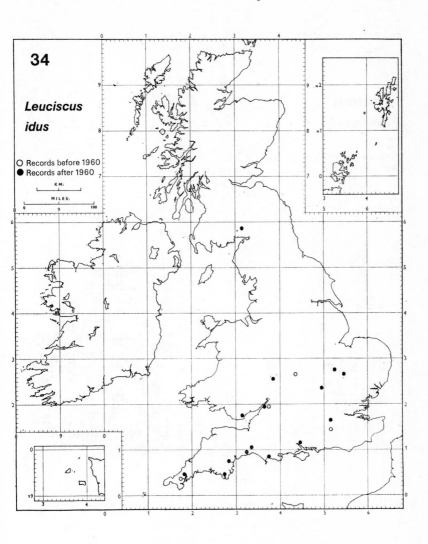

34. *Leuciscus idus*, Orfe.**

Introduced, local and rare. Clear lakes and rivers. Adult length 25–30 cm. Breeds April-July. Yellow eggs (1·5 mm) attached to weed etc. in standing or running water. Food invertebrates.

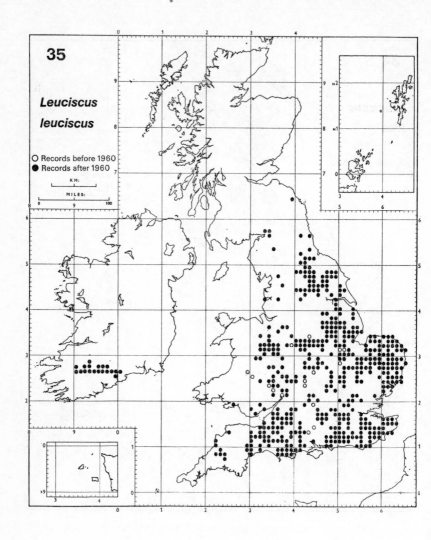

35. *Leuciscus leuciscus*, Dace.

Indigenous, fairly local but common. Rivers and streams. Adult length 15–25 cm. Breeds March-May. Yellow eggs (1·5 mm) attached to plants, etc. in running water. Food invertebrates.

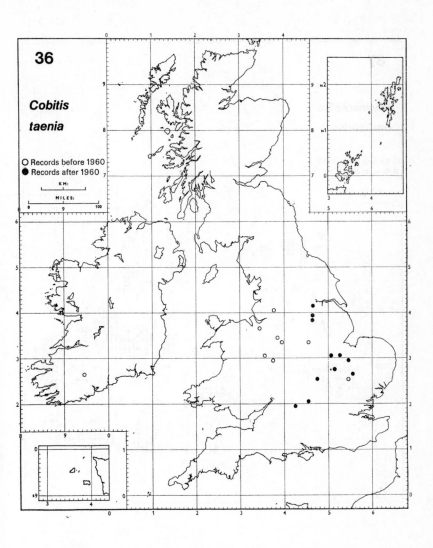

36. *Cobitis taenia*, Spined loach.**

Indigenous, local and rare. Weedy streams. Adult length 7–10 cm. Breeds April–June. Yellow eggs (0·8 mm) attached to weed in running water. Food benthic invertebrates.

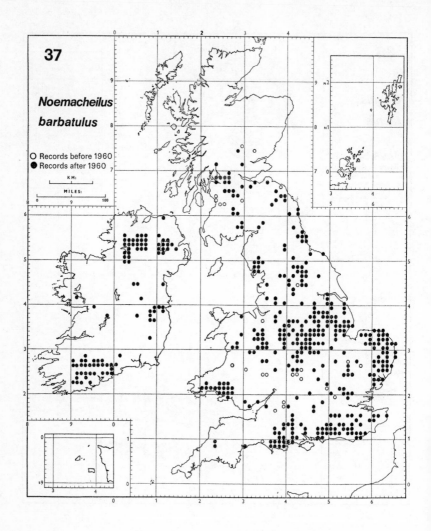

37. *Noemacheilus barbatulus,* Stone loach.

Indigenous, fairly widespread and common. Stony streams and rivers, some lakes. Adult length 8–12 cm. Breeds April-May. Yellow eggs (0·9 mm) attached to weeds and stones in running water. Food benthic invertebrates.

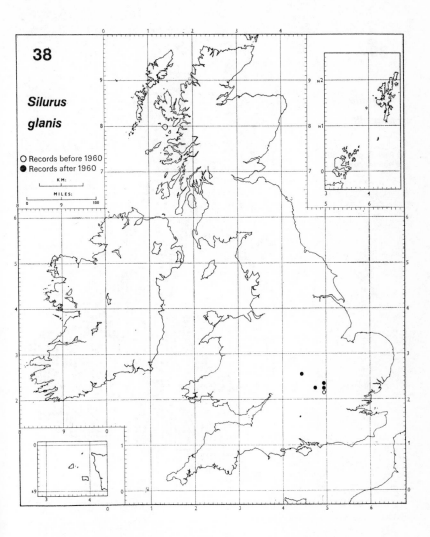

38. *Silurus glanis*, Wels.*

Introduced, very local but common. Rich, weedy lakes. Adult length 50-150 cm. Breeds May-June. Yellow eggs (3 mm) attached to weeds in standing water. Food invertebrates when small, fish and other vertebrates when larger.

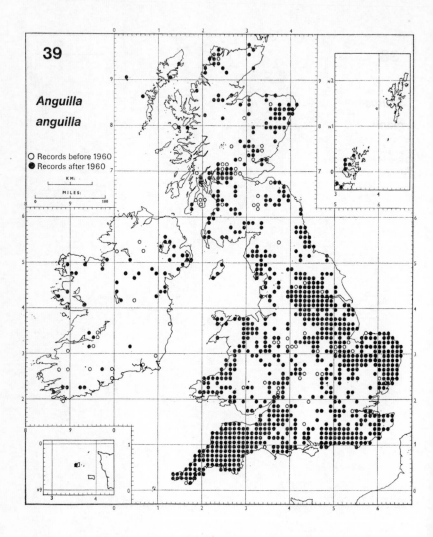

39. *Anguilla anguilla*, Eel.

Indigenous, widespread and common; catadromous. Almost all types of fresh water habitat. Adult length 40–120 cm. Breeds March–June. Clear eggs (1·0 mm) found only in the Sargasso Sea. Food invertebrates, sometimes fish.

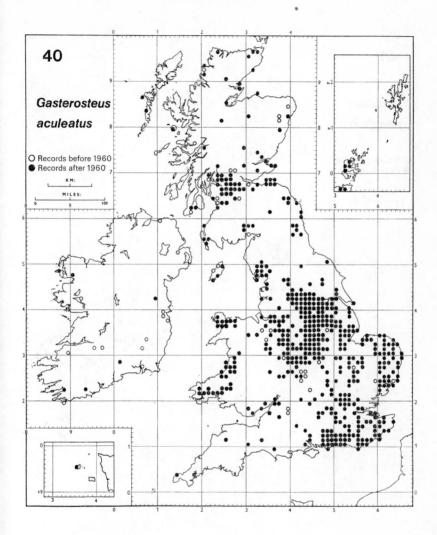

40. *Gasterosteus aculeatus*, Three-spined stickleback.

Indigenous, widespread and common. Sea shore pools, estuaries and many types of fresh water habitat. Adult length 3–6 cm. Breeds May-June. Yellow eggs (1·5 mm) in clumps in nests on silty substrata in standing or slow-flowing water. Food invertebrates.

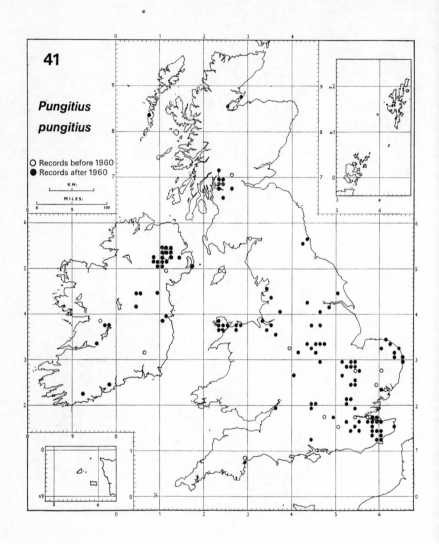

41. *Pungitius pungitius*, Ten-spined stickleback.

Indigenous, fairly widespread but sporadic, sometimes common. Estuaries and many types of fresh water habitat. Adult length 3–5 cm. Breeds March–June. Yellow eggs (1·2 mm) in clumps in nests among weed in standing or slow-flowing water. Food invertebrates.

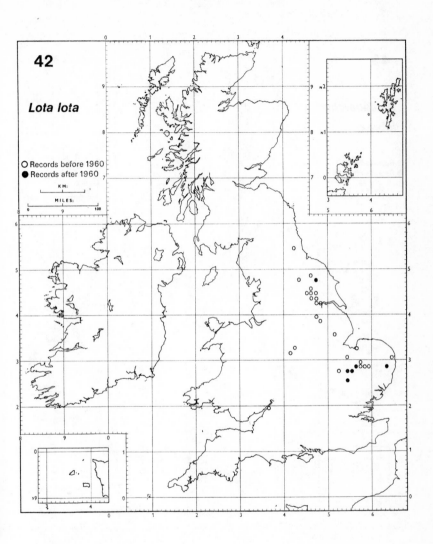

42. *Lota lota*, Burbot.**

Indigenous, very local and rare. Estuaries and lower reaches of rivers. Adult length 30–50 cm. Breeds January-March. Pale yellow eggs (1·1 mm) among stones etc. in slow-flowing water. Food invertebrates when small, invertebrates and fish when large.

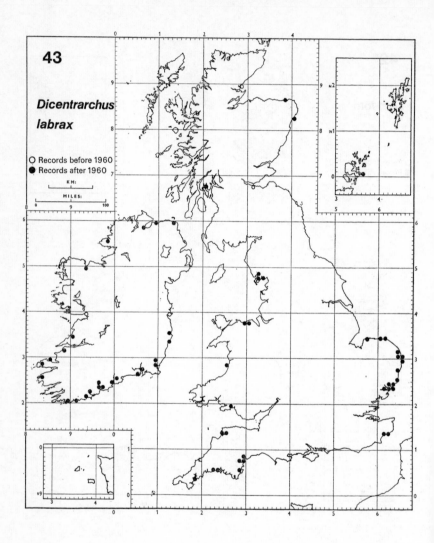

43. *Dicentrarchus labrax*, Sea bass.

Indigenous, widespread and common. Estuaries. Adult length 30–50 cm. Breeds June-August. Clear eggs (1·0 mm) attached to rocks etc. in the sea. Food invertebrates and fish.

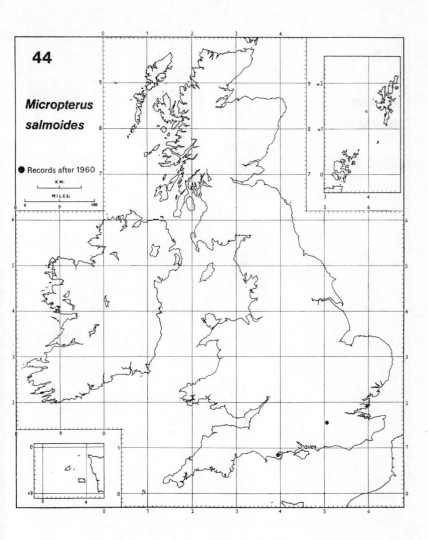

44. *Micropterus salmoides*, Largemouth bass.**

Introduced, very local and rare. Weedy lakes. Adult length 20–35 cm. Breeds March-May. Yellow eggs (2 mm) in clumps in nests on sandy areas in standing or slow flowing water. Food invertebrates when small, invertebrates and fish when large.

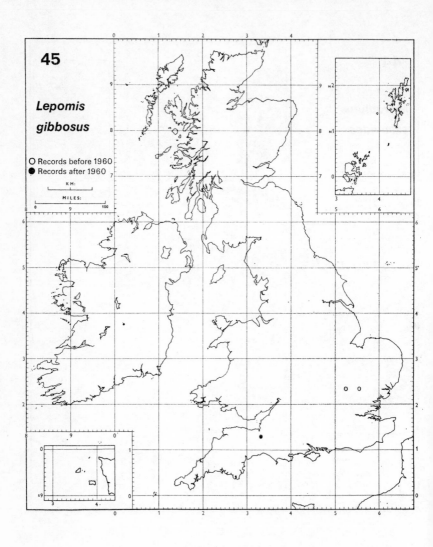

45

Lepomis
gibbosus

○ Records before 1960
● Records after 1960

KM:

MILES:

45. *Lepomis gibbosus*, Pumpkinseed.**

Introduced, very local and rare. Weedy lakes and lower reaches of rivers. Adult length 10–15 cm. Breeds May-August. Yellow eggs (2 mm) in clumps in nests on sandy areas in standing or slow-flowing water. Food invertebrates.

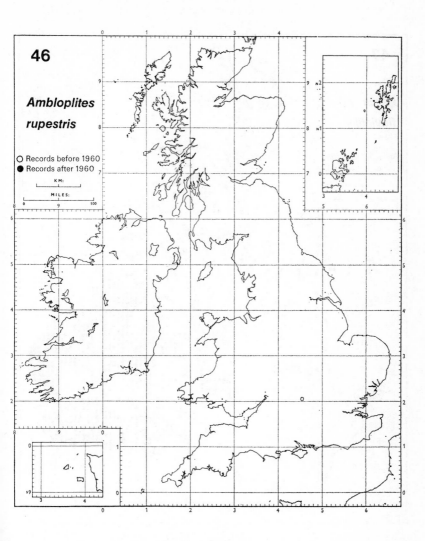

46. *Ambloplites rupestris*, Rock bass.**

Introduced, very local and rare. Weedy lakes. Adult length 12–20 cm. Breeds May-June. Yellow eggs (2 mm) in clumps in nests on sandy areas in standing or slow-flowing water. Food invertebrates.

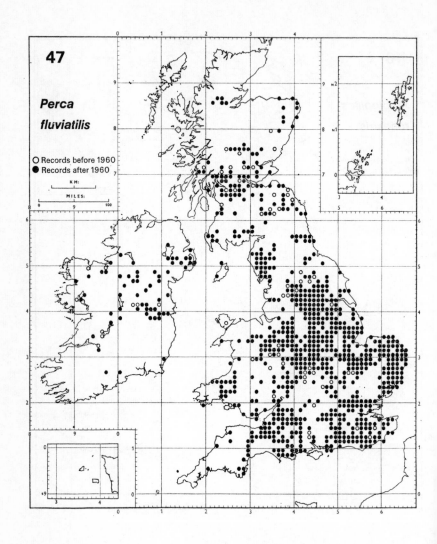

47. *Perca fluviatilis*, Perch.

Indigenous, widespread and common. Lakes, canals and slow-flowing rivers. Adult length 15–30 cm. Breeds April-June. White eggs (2·3 mm) in strands among weed in standing or slow-flowing water. Food invertebrates when small, invertebrates and fish when large.

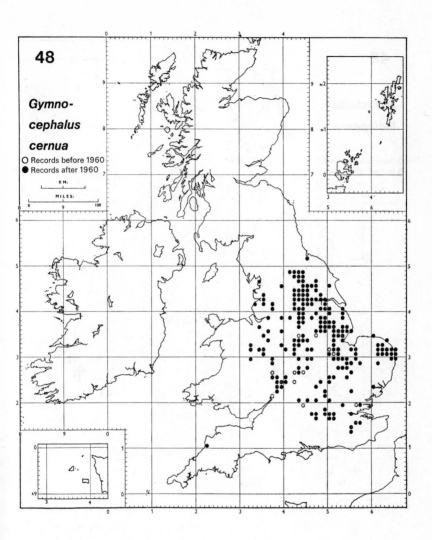

48. *Gymnocephalus cernua*, Ruffe.

Indigenous, local but common. Canals and lower reaches of rivers. Adult length 10–18 cm. Breeds March-May. Whitish-yellow eggs (0·8 mm) in clumps among weeds etc. in slow-flowing water. Food invertebrates.

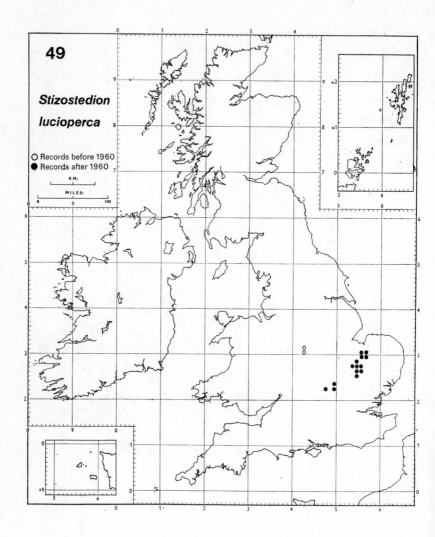

49. *Stizostedion lucioperca*, Pikeperch, zander.

Introduced, very local but quite common. Rich weedy lakes and slow-flowing rivers. Adult length 30–45 cm. Breeds April-June. Whitish-yellow eggs (1·3 mm) in clumps among plants in standing or slow-flowing water. Food invertebrates when small, fish when large.

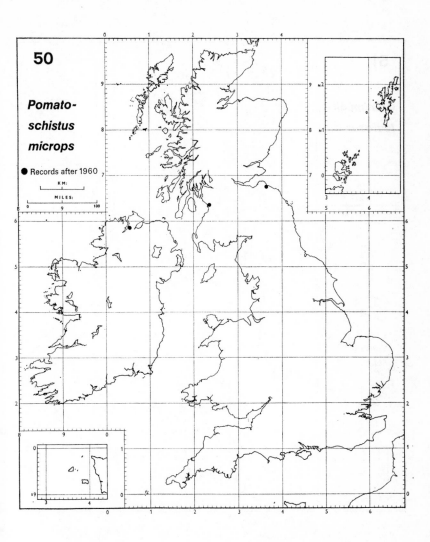

50. *Pomatoschistus microps*, Common goby.**

Indigenous, widespread and common. Estuaries, sea shore pools etc. Adult length 4–6 cm. Breeds May–July. Clear eggs (1·0 mm), oval, attached beneath stones, etc. in the sea or in brackish water. Food invertebrates.

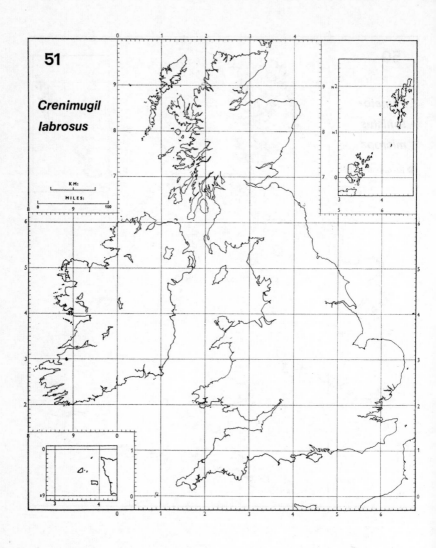

51. *Crenimugil labrosus*, Thick-lipped mullet.*

Indigenous, fairly widespread and common. Estuaries and coastal waters. Adult length 40–70 cm. Breeds April-May. Clear eggs (1·0 mm) floating in the sea. Food invertebrates.

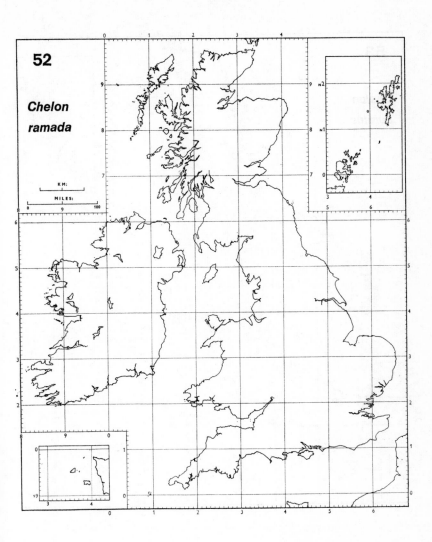

52. *Chelon ramada*, Thin-lipped mullet.*

Indigenous, fairly local and uncommon. Estuaries and coastal waters. Adult length 30–50 cm. Breeds April-May. Clear eggs (1·0 mm) floating in the sea or in brackish water. Food invertebrates.

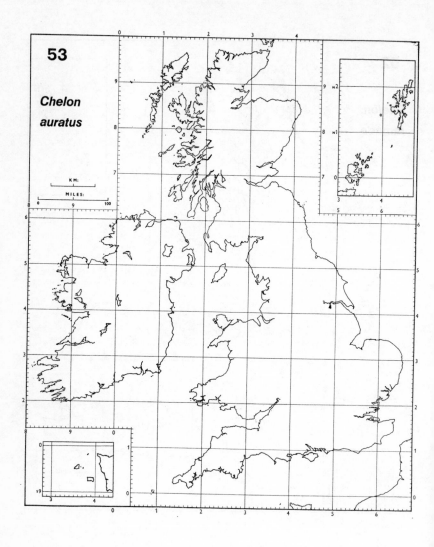

53. *Chelon auratus*, Golden mullet.*

Indigenous, fairly local and uncommon. Estuaries and coastal waters. Adult length 25–40 cm. Breeds April-May. Clear eggs (1·0 mm) floating in the sea. Food invertebrates.

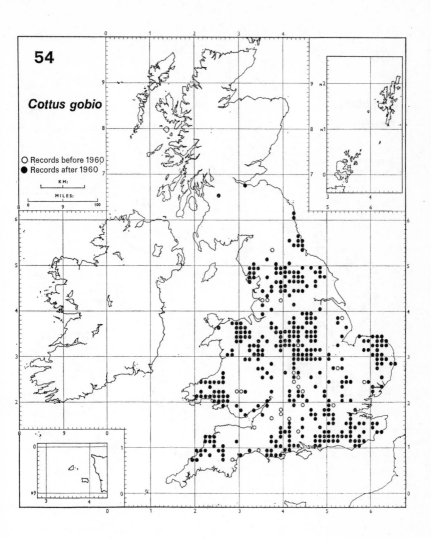

54. *Cottus gobio*, Bullhead.
   Indigenous, fairly widespread and common. Stony streams and rivers. Adult length 8–13 cm. Breeds February-May. Yellow eggs (2·3 mm) in clumps attached beneath stones in running water. Food benthic invertebrates.

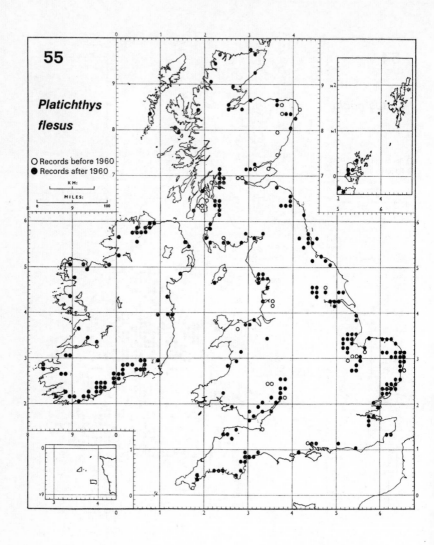

55

Platichthys

flesus

○ Records before 1960
● Records after 1960

KM:

MILES:

55. *Platichthys flesus*, Flounder.

Indigenous, widespread and common; catadromous. Estuaries and sandy rivers and lakes easily accessible from the sea. Adult length 20–40 cm. Breeds January–May. Clear eggs (0·6 mm) floating in the sea. Food benthic invertebrates.

ACKNOWLEDGMENTS

This key was produced at the suggestion of Mr H. C. Gilson, to whom I am most grateful for advice and help at all stages during its production. The manuscript has been criticised by several people among whom Mr T. B. Bagenal, Miss Jean McCormack, Dr W. E. Frost, Dr H. D. Slack, Mr A. C. Wheeler, Dr P. J. Miller, Dr D. H. Mills and Mr K. A. Pyefinch were kind enough to make useful suggestions. Only a few of the drawings were carried out by the author, the others being executed by Dr D. L. Burkel, Miss J. A. Langhorne and Mr G. M. Reid to whom I am grateful for their skill and care. In connection with the distribution maps included in this publication I would like to acknowledge the help received from the other members of the Advisory Panel on Mapping the Distribution of Freshwater Fish (Mr I. R. H. Allan, Mr T. B. Bagenal, Dr J. Banks, Mr E. D. Le Cren, Dr F. H. Perring, Mr P. H. Tombleson, Mr K. U. Vickers, Dr A. E. J. Went and Mr A. C. Wheeler) and thank them for their interest in the scheme. The maps were produced by Dr Perring and his staff at the Biological Records Centre of the Nature Conservancy, and are based on information supplied by very many people, in all parts of the country, who are too numerous to mention individually here, but without whose help our knowledge of fish distribution in this country would still be very scanty. My wife, Kathleen, has kindly read and criticised the manuscript of this publication.

ACKNOWLEDGMENTS

REFERENCES

Balinsky, B. I. (1948). On the development of specific characters in cyprinid fishes. *Proc. zool. Soc. Lond.,* **118**, 335-44.

Bracken, J. J. & Kennedy, M. P. (1967). A key to the identification of the eggs and young stages of coarse fish in Irish waters. *Scient. Proc. R. Dubl. Soc.,* **2**, 99-108.

Davis, F. M. (1936). An account of the fishing gear of England and Wales. *Fishery Invest., Lond.,* **15**, 1-139.

Day, F. (1880). *The fishes of Great Britain and Ireland.* London.

Evans, A. (1952). *Aquariums.* London.

Graham, M. (1956). *Sea fisheries. Their investigation in the United Kingdom.* London.

Jenkins, J. T. (1936). *The fishes of the British Isles.* London.

Maitland, P. S. (1969). A preliminary account of the mapping of the distribution of freshwater fish in the British Isles. *J. Fish Biol.,* **1**, 45-58.

Meadows, B. S. (1968). On the occurrence of the Guppy *Lebistes reticulatus* in the River Lee. *Essex Nat.,* **32**, 186-89.

Owen, G. (1955). The use of propylene phenoxetol as a relaxing agent. *Nature, Lond.,* **175**, 434.

Perring, F. H. & Walters, S. M. (1962). *Atlas of the British flora.* London.

Regan, C. T. (1911). *The freshwater fishes of the British Isles.* London.

Rounsefell, G. A. & Everhardt, W. H. (1953). *Fishery science: its methods and applications.* New York.

Schindler, O. (1957). *Guide to freshwater fishes.* London.

Spillman, C. J. (1961). Poissons d'eau douce. *Faune de France,* **65.** Paris.

Sterba, G. (1962). Die Neunaugen (Petromyzonidae). *Handb. Binnenfisch. Mitteleur.,* **3B**, 263–352.

Varley, M. E. (1967). *British freshwater fishes: factors affecting their distribution.* London.

Wheeler, A. C. (1969). *The fishes of the British Isles and North-West Europe.* London.

SPECIES INDEX

Page numbers in **bold** refer to illustrations; those in *italics* refer to distribution maps and ecological notes.

DORSET COUNTY LIBRARY

Headquarters: Colliton Park, Dorchester, Dorset

Telephone: Dorchester 3131

Evenings and Saturdays: Dorchester 3723

This book must be returned or renewed on or before the last date marked above. Unless required by other readers, books may be renewed by post or telephone, quoting the last date **stamped**, author, title and classification number.

Please keep this book clean, protect it from rain and extreme heat, and do not turn down the corners of its leaves or spoil it by pencil or other marks.

Change of address of reader must be notified immediately.